THE INVISIBLE PYRAMID

WOODCUTS BY WALTER FERRO

THE
INVISIBLE
PYRAMID

by Loren Eiseley

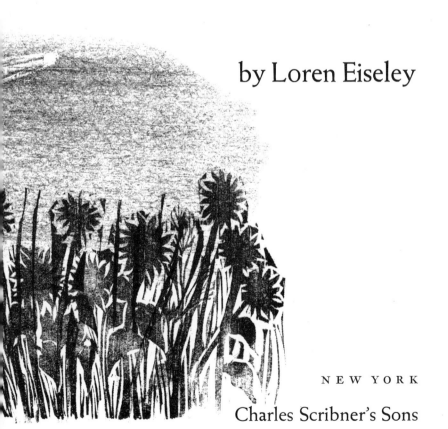

NEW YORK

Charles Scribner's Sons

DEDICATED TO THE MEMORY OF

FRANK G. SPECK

TO ME,

THE LAST MAGICIAN

PREFACE

THE theme of this book was developed through a series of lectures delivered under the auspices of the John Danz Fund at the University of Washington in Seattle in the Fall of 1969. It gives me pleasure to express to the members of the Danz family my appreciation of their interest and generosity, as well as to the administrative staff of the University, who were my hosts.

I should also like to express my thanks to my friend and former colleague, the astronomer Frank Bradshaw Wood, of the University of Florida, Gainesville, for information cheerfully supplied me upon the elliptic of Halley's comet. Similarly I am glad to seize this opportunity to mention the many provocative conversations which have taken place with my university colleagues, Froelich Rainey, Director of the University Museum, and Dale Coman, M.D., of the University Medical School. As men concerned with the growing problems of our environment, we share equal anxieties and hopes.

In this book I have chosen, for literary reasons extending into the seventeenth century, to use somewhat interchangeably the terms Halley's star and Halley's comet, since for the latter no satisfactory synonym exists. There was a time when all the visible heavenly bodies were viewed pretty much the same. The use of "falling stars" to indicate meteor showers persists today. I do not think anyone will be confused by this interchange, which has stylistic advantages in a book of this nature.

CONTENTS

THE INVISIBLE PYRAMID

Once in a cycle the comet
Doubles its lonesome track.
Enriched with the tears of a thousand years,
Aeschylus wanders back.

—JOHN G. NEIHARDT

PROLOGUE

Man would not be man if his dreams did not exceed his grasp. If, in this book, I choose to act in the ambivalent character of pessimist and optimist, it is because mankind itself plays a similar contradictory role upon the stage of life. Like John Donne, man lies in a close prison, yet it is dear to him. Like Donne's, his thoughts at times overleap the sun and pace beyond the body. If I term humanity a slime mold organism it is because our present environment suggests it. If I remember the sunflower forest it is because from its hidden reaches man arose. The green world is his sacred center. In moments of sanity he must still seek refuge there.

If I dream by contrast of the eventual drift of the star voyagers through the dilated time of the universe, it is because I have seen thistledown off to new worlds and am at heart a voyager who, in this modern time, still yearns for the lost country of his birth. As an anthropologist I know that we exist in the morning twilight of humanity and pray that we may survive its noon. The travail of the men of my profession is to delve amid the fragments of civilizations irretrievably lost and, at the same time, to know man's enormous capacity to create.

But I dream, and because I dream, I severally condemn, fear, and salute the future. It is the salute of a gladiator ringed by the indifference of the watching stars. Man himself is the solitary arbiter of his own defeats and victories. I have mused on the dead of all epochs from flint to steel. They fought blindly and well against the future, or the cities and ourselves would not be here. Now all about us, unseen, the final desperate engagement continues.

If man goes down I do not believe that he will ever again have the resources or the strength to defend the sunflower forest and simultaneously to follow the beckoning road across the star fields. It is now or never for both, and the price is very high. It may be, as A. E. Housman said, that we breathe the air that kills both at home and afar. He did not speak of pollution; he spoke instead of the death that comes with memory. I have wondered how long the social memory of a great culture can be sustained without similarly growing lethal. This also our century may decide.

I confess that the air that kills has been breathed upon the pages of this book, but upon it also has shone the silver light of flying thistledown. In the heart of the city I have heard the wild geese crying on the pathways that lie over a vanished forest. Nature has not changed the force that drives them. Man, too, is a different expression of that natural force. He has fought his way from the sea's depths to Palomar Mountain. He has mastered the plague. Now, in some final Armageddon, he confronts himself.

As a boy I once rolled dice in an empty house, playing against myself. I suppose I was afraid. It was twilight, and

I forget who won. I was too young to have known that the old abandoned house in which I played was the universe. I would play for man more fiercely if the years would take me back.

ONE ❖ THE STAR DRAGON

*Already at the origin of the species man was
equal to what he was destined to become.*

—JEAN ROSTAND

THE STAR DRAGON

In the year 1910 Halley's comet—the comet that among many visitations had flared in 1066 over the Norman invasion of England—was again brightening the night skies of earth. "Menace of the Skies," shrieked the more lurid newspapers.

Like hundreds of other little boys of the new century, I was held up in my father's arms under the cottonwoods of a cold and leafless spring to see the hurtling emissary of the void. My father told me something then that is one of my earliest and most cherished memories.

"If you live to be an old man," he said carefully, fixing my eyes on the midnight spectacle, "you will see it again. It will come back in seventy-five years. Remember," he whispered in my ear, "I will be gone, but you will see it. All that time it will be traveling in the dark, but somewhere, far out there"—he swept a hand toward the blue horizon of the plains—"it will turn back. It is running glittering through millions of miles."

I tightened my hold on my father's neck and stared uncomprehendingly at the heavens. Once more he spoke against my ear and for us two alone. "Remember, all you have to do is to be careful and wait. You will be seventy-eight or seventy-nine years old. I think you will live to see it—for me," he whispered a little sadly with the foreknowledge that was part of his nature.

"Yes, Papa," I said dutifully, having little or no grasp of seventy-five years or millions of miles on the floorless pathways of space. Nevertheless I was destined to recall the incident all my life. It was out of love for a sad man who clung to me as I to him that, young though I was, I remembered. There are long years still to pass, and already I am breathing like a tired runner, but the voice still sounds in my ears and I know with the sureness of maturity that the great wild satellite has reversed its course and is speeding on its homeward journey toward the sun.

At four I had been fixed with the compulsive vertigo of vast distance and even more endless time. I had received, through inherited temperament and inclination, a nostalgic admonition to tarry. Besides, I had given what amounted to a desperate promise. "Yes, Papa," I had said with the generosity of childhood, not knowing the chances that men faced in life. This year, after a visit to my doctor, I had written anxiously to an astronomer friend. "Brad," I had asked, "where is Halley's comet reported on the homeward track? I know it must have turned the elliptic, but where do you calculate it now, how far—and how long, how long—?"

I have his answer before me. "You're pushing things, old man," he writes. "Don't expect us to see it yet—you're too young. The orbit is roughly eighteen astronomical units or one billion six hundred and fifty million miles. It headed back this way probably in nineteen forty-eight."

Nineteen forty-eight. I grope wearily amidst memories of the Cold War, Korea, the Berlin blockade, spies, the impossible-to-be-kept secrets of the atom. All that time through the black void the tiny pinpoint of light has been hurrying, hurrying, running faster than I, thousands of miles faster as it curves toward home. Because of my father and the promise I had made, a kind of personal bond has been projected between me and the comet. I do not think of what it heralded over Hastings in 1066. I think it is racing sunward so that I can see it stretched once more across the heavens and momently restore the innocence of 1910.

But there is inner time, "personal, private chronometry," a brain surgeon once told me. There is also outer time that harries us ruthlessly to our deaths. Some nights in a dark room, staring at the ceiling, I can see the light like a mote in my eye, like a far-off train headlight glimpsed long ago as a child on the prairies of the West. The mournful howl of the train whistle echoes in my head and mingles with the night's black spaces. The voice is that of the comet as I hear it, climbing upward on the arc of space. At last in the dark I compose myself for sleep. I pull the blanket up to my chin and think of radar ceaselessly sweeping the horizon, and the intercontinental missiles resting in their blast-hardened pits.

But no, I dream deeper, slipping back like a sorcerer through the wood of time. Life was no better, not even as safe, proportionately, in the neolithic hill forts whose tiny trenches can be seen from the air over the British downs. A little band of men, with their families beside them, crouched sleepless with ill-made swords, awaiting an at-

The Star Dragon * 9

tack at dawn. And before that, the caves and the freezing cold, with the ice creeping ever southward autumn by autumn.

The dead we buried in red ochre under the fire pit, the red standing for blood, for we were quick in analogies and magic. The ochre was for life elsewhere and farewell. We tramped away in our furred garb and the leaves and snow washed over the place of our youth. We worked always toward the south across the tundra following the long trail of the mammoth. Someone saw a vast flame in the sky and pointed, but it was not called Halley's comet then. You could see it glinting through the green light and the falling snow.

Farther backward still across twin ice advances and two long interglacial summers. We were cruder now, our eyes wild and uncertain, less sure that we were men. We no longer had sewn garments, and our only weapon was a heavy pointed stone, unhafted and held in the hand. Even our faces had taken on the cavernous look of the places we inhabited. There were difficulties about making fire, and we could not always achieve it. The dead were left where they fell. Women wept less, and the bands were smaller. Our memories consisted of dim lights under heavy sockets of bone. We did not paint pictures, or increase, by magic, the slain beasts. We talked, but the words we needed were fewer. Often we went hungry. It was a sturdy child that survived. We meant well but we were terrifyingly igno-rant and given to frustrated anger. There was too much locked up in us that we could not express.

We were being used, and perhaps it was against this that we unconsciously raged the most. We were neither beast nor man. We were only a bridge transmitting life. I say we were almost animals and knew little, but this we felt and raged against. There were no words to help us. No one could think of them. Sometimes we were stalked by the huge cats, but it was the inner stalking that was most terrible. I saw a star in the sky with a flaming tail and cowered, shaking, into a bush, making uncouth sounds. It is not laughable. Animals do not do this. They do not see the world as we do—even we.

I think we are now well across the last ice, toward the beginning. There is no fire of any sort but we do not miss it. We are far to the south and the climate is warm. We have no tools except an occasional bone club. We walk upright, but I think we are now animals. We are small—pygmies, in fact. We wear no clothes. We no longer stare at the stars or think of the unreal. The dead are dead. No one follows us at nightfall. Do not repeat this. I think we are animals. I think we have reached beyond the bridge. We are happy here. Tell no one.

I sigh in my sleep but I cannot hold to the other side of the bridge—the animal side. The comet turns blazing on its far run into space. Slowly I plod once more with the furred ones up the ladder of time. We cross one ice and then another. There is much weeping, too much of memory. It is all to do over again and go on. The white-robed men think well in Athens. I heard a man named Pindar acclaim something that implied we have a likeness to the immortals. "What course after nightfall," he questioned, "has destiny written that we must run to the end?"

What course after nightfall? I have followed the comet's track returning and returning while our minds and our bodies changed. The comet will appear once more. I will follow it that far. Then I will no longer be part of the bridge. Perhaps I will be released to go back. Time and space are my inheritance from my father and the star. I will climb no further up the ladder of fiery return. I will go forward only one more rung. What will await me there is not pleasant, but it is in the star's destiny as well as mine. I lie awake once more on the dark bed. I feel my heart beating, and wait for the hurrying light.

II

In 1804, well over a century and a half ago, Captain William Clark recorded in his diary far up the unknown Missouri that ahead of the little expedition that he shared with Meriwether Lewis hung a formidable curtain of blowing dust through which they could not see.

"Tell us what is new," the few savants in the newborn American republic had advised the explorers when they departed westward. Men continued to have strange expectations of what lay hidden in the still uncharted wilds behind the screen of the great eastern forest. Some thought that the mammoth, whose bones had been found at Big Bone Lick, in Kentucky, might still wander alive and trumpeting in that vast hinterland. The "dreadful curtain" through which the youthful captains peered on that cold, forbidding day in January could have hidden anything. Indeed the cloud itself was symbolic. It represented time in inconceivable quantities—time, not safe, not contained in Christian quantity, but rather vast as the elemental dust storm itself.

The dust in those remote regions was the dust of ice ages, of mountains wearing away under the splintering of frost and sun. The Platte was slowly carrying a mountain range to the sea over giant fans of gravel. Frémont's men would later report the strange and grotesque sculptures of the wind in stone. It was true that a few years earlier the Scottish physician James Hutton had philosophically conceived such time as possible. His views had largely proved unwelcome and had been dismissed in Europe. On the far-western divide, however, amid the roar of waters falling toward an unknown western ocean, men, frontiersmen though they were, must have felt with an increasing tinge of awe the weight of ages unknown to man.

Huge bones bulked in the exposed strata and were measured with wonder. No man knew their names or their antiquity. New things the savants had sought surrounded the explorers, not in the sense of the living survival of great elephants but rather in the sense of a vaster novelty—the extension of time itself. It was as though man for the first time was intruding upon some gigantic stage not devised for him. Among these wastes one felt as though inhuman actors had departed, as though the drama of life had reached an unexpected climax.

One catches this same lost feeling in the remarks of another traveler, Alexis de Tocqueville, venturing into the virgin forest far from the pruned orchards of France. "Here," he said, "man seems to enter life furtively. Everything enters into a silence so profound, a stillness so complete that the soul feels penetrated by a sort of religious terror." Even in the untouched forest, time had taken on this same American quality: "Immense trees," de Tocqueville wrote in awe, "retained by the surrounding branches, hang suspended in the air and fall into dust without touching the earth."

It is perhaps a significant coincidence that man's full recognition of biological novelty, of the invisible transformations of the living substance itself, came close upon the heels of the discovery of the vast wilderness stage which still held the tumbled bones of the former actors. It was a domain which had remained largely unknown to Europeans. Sir Charles Lyell, who, in the 1830s, successfully revived Hutton's lost doctrines of geological antiquity, visited the United States in the 1840s and lectured here to enthralled thousands. Finally, it was Charles Darwin, the voyager-naturalist, who, as a convinced follower of Lyell, had gazed upon a comparable wilderness in South America and had succeeded, in his mind's eye, in peopling the abandoned stage with the creatures of former epochs. It was almost as though Europe, though rife with speculation since the time of the great voyagers, could not quite escape its man-centeredness or its preoccupation with civilized hedgerows and formal gardens. Its thinkers had still to breathe, like Darwin, the thin air of Andean highlands, or hear the falling of stones in mountain cataracts.

To see his role on the world stage, Western man had twice to revise his conception of time: once from the brevity of a few thousand years to eons of inconceivable antiquity, and, a second time, with far more difficulty, to perceive that this lengthened time-span was peopled with wraiths and changing cloud forms. Time was not just aged rocks and trees, alike since the beginning of creation; its living aspect did not consist merely of endless Oriental cycles of civilizations rising and declining. Instead, the living flesh itself was alterable. Our seeming stability of form was an illusion fostered by the few millennia of written history. Behind that history lay the vast and unrecorded gloom of ice ages inhabited by the great beasts which the explorers, at Thomas Jefferson's bidding, had sought through the blowing curtain of the dust.

Man, but not man in the garb we know, had cracked marrow bones in those dim shadows before his footprints vanished amidst the grass of wild savannahs. For interminable ages winged reptiles had hovered over the shores of ancient seas; creatures still more strange had paddled in the silence of enormous swamps. Finally, in that long backward range of time, it was possible to emerge upon shores which no longer betrayed signs of life, because life had become mere potential.

At that point one could have seen life as the novelty it truly is. "Tell us what is new," reiterated the eager scientists to the explorers. Past mid-century, an answer could be made. It was life itself that was eternally, constantly new. Dust settled and blew the same from age to age; mountains were worn down to rise again. Only life, that furtive intruder drifting across marsh and field and mountain, altered its masks upon the age-old stage. And as the masks were discarded they did not come again as did the lava of the upthrust mountain cores. Species died as individuals died, or, if they did not perish, they were altered beyond recognition and recall. Man cannot restore the body that once shaped his mind. The bird upon the bough cannot, any more than a summer's yellow butterfly, again materialize the chrysalis from which it sprang.

Indeed, in the end, life can be seen not only as a novelty moving through time toward an endlessly diverging series of possible futures but also as a complete phantom. If we had only the scattered chemicals of the cast-off forms and no experience in ourselves of life's existence, we would not be able to identify its reality or its mutability by any chemical test known to us. The only thing which infuses a handful of dust with such uncanny potential is our empirical knowledge that the phenomenon called life exists, and that it constantly pursues an unseen arrow which is irreversible.

Through the anatomical effort and puzzle-fitting of many men, time, by the mid-nineteenth century, had become gigantic. When *On the Origin of Species* was published, the great stage was seen not alone to have been playing to remote, forgotten audiences; the actors themselves still went masked into a future no man could anticipate. Some straggled out and died in the wings. But still the play persisted. As one watched, one could see that the play had one very strange quality about it: the characters, most of them, began in a kind of generous latitude of living space and ended by being pinched out of existence in a grimy corner.

Once in a while, it is true, a prisoner escaped just when all seemed over for him. This happened when some oxygen-starved Devonian fish managed to stump ashore on their fins and become the first vertebrate invaders of the land. By and large, however, the evolutionary story had a certain unhappy quality.

The evolutionary hero became a victim of his success and then could not turn backward; he prospered and grew too large and was set upon by clever enemies evolving about him. Or he specialized in diet, and the plants upon which he fed became increasingly rare. Or he survived at the cost of shutting out the light and eating his way into living rock like some mollusks. Or he hid in deserts and survived through rarity and supersensitive ears. In cold climates he reduced his temperature with the season, dulled his heart to long-drawn spasmodic effort, and slept most of his life away. Or, parasitically, he slumbered in the warm intestinal darkness of the tapeworm's eyeless world.

Restricted and dark were many of these niches, and equally dark and malignant were some of the survivors. The oblique corner with no outlet had narrowed upon them all. Biological evolution could be defined as one long series of specializations—hoofs that prevented hands, wings that, while opening the wide reaches of the air, prevented the manipulation of tools. The list was endless. Each creature was a tiny fraction of the life force; the greater portion had died with the environments that created them. Others had continued to evolve, but always their transformations seemed to present a more skilled adaptation to an increasingly narrow corridor of existence. Success too frequently meant specialization, and specialization, ironically, was the beginning of the road to extinction. This was the essential theme that time had dramatized upon the giant stage.

III

It may now appear that I have been wandering mentally amidst irrelevant and strange events—time glimpsed through a blowing curtain of dust, and, among fallen stones and badland pinnacles, bones denoting not just the erosion of ages but the mysterious transformation of living bodies.

Man after man in the immediately post-Darwinian days would stare into his mirror at the bony contours of a skull that held some grinning secret beyond the simple fact of death. Anatomists at the dissecting table would turn up odd vestigial muscles and organs. Our bodies held out-dated machinery as strange as that to be found in the attics of old houses. Into these anatomical depths few would care to probe. But there were scholars who were not averse to delving among fossils, and the skulls they found or diagnosed would multiply. These would be recognized at last for what they were, the dropped masks of the beginning of Nature's last great play—the play of man.

Strangely, it is a different play, though made partly of old ingredients. In three billion years of life upon the planet, this play had never been acted upon the great stage before. We come at a unique moment in geological history, and we ourselves are equally unique. We have brought with us out of the forest darkness a new unprophesiable world—a latent, lurking universe within our heads.

In the world of Charles Darwin, evolution was particulate; it contained and traced the history of fins, claws, wings, and teeth. The Darwinian circle was immersed in the study of the response of the individual organism to its environment, and the selective impact of the environment upon its creatures. By contrast, just as biological evolution had brought the magic of the endlessly new in organic form, so the evolving brain, through speech, had literally created a superorganic structure unimaginable until its emergence.

Alfred Russel Wallace, Darwin's contemporary, perceived that with the emergence of the human brain, man had, to a previously inconceivable degree, passed out of the domain of the particulate evolution of biological organs and had entered upon what we may call history. Human beings, in whom the power of communication had arisen, were leaving the realm of phylogeny for the realm of history, which was to contain, henceforth, our final destiny. After three billion years of biological effort, man alone had seemingly evaded the oblique trap of biological specialization. He had done so by the development of a specialized organ—the brain—whose essential purpose was to evade specialization.

The tongue and the hand, so disproportionately exaggerated in his motor cortex, were to be its primary instruments. With these he would elude channelized instinct and channelized organic development. The creature who had dropped from some long-ago tree into the grass had managed to totter upright and free the grasping forelimb. Brain, hand, and tongue would henceforth evolve together. Fin, fur, and paw would vanish into the mists of the past. Henceforth it would be the brain that clothed and unclothed man. Fire would warm him, flint would strike for him, vessels would carry him over dangerous waters.

In the end, with the naked body of an awkward and hastily readjusted climber, he would plumb the seas' depths and mount, with wings spun in his brain, the heights of air. Enormous computations upon the movements of far bodies in space would roll in seconds from his computers. His great machines would leap faster at his bidding than the slower speed of his own nerves.

Because of speech, drawn from an infinitesimal spark along a nerve end, the vague, ill-defined surroundings of the animal world would be transformed, named, and categorized. Mind would reach into a past before its becoming; the misty future experienced by dim animal instinct would leap into sudden, clear perspective. Language, whose constituents have come down the long traverse of millennia as rolled and pounded by circumstance as a flint ax churned in a river bed, leaves no direct traces of its dim beginnings. With the first hieroglyph, oral tradition would become history. Out of a spoken sound, man's first and last source of inexhaustible power, would emerge the phantom world which the anthropologist prosaically calls culture. Its bridges, its towers, and its lightnings lie potential in a little globe of gray matter that can fade and blow away on any wind. The novelty of evolutionary progression through time has begotten another novelty, the novelty of history, the evolutionary flow of ideas in the heads of men.

The role of the brain is analogous in a distant way to the action of mutation in generating improbabilities in the organic realm. Moreover, the human brain appears to be a remarkably solitary product of this same organic process which, in actuality, it has transcended. In this sense life has produced a newly emergent instrument capable of transmitting a greatly speeded-up social heredity based not upon the gene but instead upon communication. In its present technological phase it has brought the ends of the world into conflict and at the same time is reaching outward into space.

About ourselves there always lingers a penumbral rainbow—what A. L. Kroeber termed the superorganic—that cloud of ideas, visions, institutions which hover about, indeed constitute human society, but which can be dissected from no single brain. This rainbow, which exists in all heads and dies with none, is the essential part of man. Through it he becomes what we call human, and not otherwise.

Man is not a creature to be contained in a solitary skull vault, nor is he measurable as, say, a saber-toothed cat or a bison is measurable. Something, the rainbow dancing before his eyes, the word uttered by the cave fire at evening, eludes us and runs onward. It is gone when we come with our spades upon the cold ashes of the campfire four hundred thousand years removed.

Paradoxically, the purpose of the human brain is to escape physical specialization by the projections of thought. There is no parallel organism with which to compare ourselves. The creature from which we arose has perished. On the direct hominid line there is no twilight world of living fossils which we can subject to examination. At best we are forced to make inferences from less closely related primates whose activities lie below the threshold of speech.

The nineteenth century, in the efforts of men like Hughlings Jackson, came to see the brain as an organ whose primary parts had been laid down successively in evolutionary time, a little like the fossil strata in the earth itself. The centers of conscious thought were the last superficial deposit on the surface of a more ancient and instinctive brain. As the roots of our phylogenetic tree pierce deep into earth's past, so our human consciousness is similarly embedded in, and in part constructed of, pathways which were laid down before man in his present form existed. To acknowledge this fact is still to comprehend as little of the brain's true secrets as an individual might understand of the dawning of his own consciousness from a single egg cell.

The long, slow turn of world-time as the geologist has known it, and the invisibly moving hour hand of evolution perceived only yesterday by the biologist, have given way in the human realm to a fantastically accelerated social evolution induced by industrial technology. So fast does this change progress that a growing child strives to master the institutional customs of a society which, compared with the pace of past history, compresses centuries of change into his lifetime. I myself, like others of my generation, was born in an age which has already perished. At my death I will look my last upon a nation which, save for some linguistic continuity, will seem increasingly alien and remote. It will be as though I peered upon my youth through misty centuries. I will not be merely old; I will be a genuine fossil embedded in onrushing man-made time before my actual death.

IV

"There never was a first man or a first primate," Dr. Glenn Jepsen of Princeton once remarked iconoclastically. The distinguished paleontologist then added that the "billions of genetic filaments in our ancestral phyletic cord are of many lengths, no two precisely the same. We have not had our oversized brain very long but the pentadactyl pattern of our extremities originated deep in . . . the Paleozoic." Moreover, we have, of late, discovered that our bipedal, man-ape ancestors seem to have flourished for a surprisingly long time without any increase in their cranial content whatever—some four or five million years, in fact.

It used to be thought that the brain of proto-man would have had to develop very early to enable him to survive upright upon the ground at all. Oddly, it now appears that man survived so well under these circumstances that it is difficult to say why, in the end, he became man at all. His bipedal pre-man phase lasted much longer—five or six times at least—than his whole archaeological history down to this very moment. What makes the whole story so mystifying is that the expansion of his neurocranium took place relatively rapidly during the million years or so of Ice Age time, and has not been traced below this point. The supposed weak-bodied creature whom Darwin nervously tried to fit into his conception of the war of nature on the continents is thought to have romped through a longer geological time period than his large-brained descendants may ever see.

We know that at least two million years ago the creature could make some simple use of stones and bones and may possibly have fashioned crude windbreaks. He was still small-brained in human terms, however, and if his linguistic potentialities were increasing there remains no satisfactory evidence of the fact. Thus we are confronted with the question why man, as we know him, arose, and why, having arisen, he found his way out of the green confines of his original world. Not all the human beings even of our existing species did. Though their brains are comparable to our own, they have lingered on, something less than one per cent of today's populations, at the edge of a morning twilight that we have forgotten. There can thus be no ready assertion that man's departure from his first world, the world of chameleon-like shifts and forest changes, was either ordained or inevitable. Neither can it be said that visible tools created brains. Some of the forest peoples—though clever to adapt—survive with a paucity of technical equipment.

As to why our pygmoid ancestors, or, more accurately, some group of them, took the road to larger brains we do not know. Most of the suggestions made would just as readily fit a number of non-human primate forms which did not develop large brains. Our line is gone, and while the behavior of our existing relatives is worth examination we cannot unravel out of another genetic strand the complete story of our own.

Not without interest is the fact that much of this development is correlated with the advances and recessions of the continental ice fields. It is conceivable, at least, that some part of the human stock was being exposed during this time to relentless genetic pressures and then, in interglacial times, to renewed relaxation of barriers and consequent genetic mixture. A few scattered finds from remote portions of the Euro-Asiatic land mass will never clarify this suspicion. For hundreds of thousands of years of crucial human history we have not a single bone as a document.

There is another curious thing about the Ice Age. Except for the emergence of genuinely modern man toward the close of its icy winter, it is an age of death, not a birth time of species. Extinction has always followed life relentlessly through the long eras of earth's history. The Pleistocene above all else was a time of great extinctions. Many big animals perished, and though man's hunting technology was improving, his numbers were still modest. He did not then possess the capacity to ravage continents in the way he was later to do.

The dinosaurs vanished before man appeared on earth, and their disappearance has caused much debate. They died out over a period many millions of years in extent and at a time when the low warm continents lapped by inland seas were giving way to bleaker highlands. The events of the Ice Age are markedly different. First of all, many big mammals—mammoth, mastodon, sloth, long-horned bison—survived the great ice sheets only to die at their close. It is true that man, by then dispersing over the continents, may have had something to do with their final extermination, but there perished also certain creatures like the dire wolves, in which man could have taken little direct interest.

We are thus presented, in contrast to the situation at the close of the age of reptiles, with a narrowly demarcated line of a few thousand years in which a great variety of earth's northern fauna died out while man survived. Along with the growing desiccation in Southwest Asia, these extinctions gave man, the hunter, a mighty push outside his original game-filled Eden. He had to turn to plant domestication to survive, and plants, it just happens, are the primary road to a settled life and the basic supplies from which cities and civilizations arise. A half-dying green kingdom, one might say, forced man out of a relationship which might otherwise have continued down to the present.

But, the question persists, why did so many creatures die in so little time after marching back and forth with the advancing or retreating ice through so many thousand years? Just recently the moon voyage has hinted at a possible clue, though it must be ventured very tentatively when man's observational stay upon the moon has been so short.

The Apollo 11 astronauts observed and succeeded in photographing melted or glazed droplets concentrated on points and edges of moon rock. Dr. Thomas Gold, director of Cornell University's Center for Radio Physics, has suggested that these glasslike concretions are evidence of melting, produced by a giant solar flare activated for only a few moments, but of an unexpected intensity. Giant storms are known to lick outward from the sun's surface, but a solar disturbance of the magnitude required to account for such a melting—if it was indeed sun-produced—would have seemed from earth like the flame of a dragon's breath. Most of the ultraviolet of the sun-storm, generated perhaps by a comet hurtling into the sun's surface, would have been absorbed by the earth's atmosphere. A temperature effect on earth need not have been pronounced so long as the flare was momentary. The unprotected surface of the moon, however, would have received the full impact of the dragon's tongue.

Dr. Gold has calculated by various means that the event, if actually produced by a solar flare, lies somewhere close to thirty thousand years from us in time and is therefore unrecorded in the annals of man. But here is the curious thing. The period involved lies in the closing Ice Age, in the narrow time zone of vast extinctions in the northern hemisphere. Was the giant flare, an unheard-of phenomenon, in some way involved with the long dying of certain of the great mammals that followed? Seemingly the earth escaped visible damage because of its enveloping blanket of air. No living man knows what the flicking tongue of a dragon star might do, however, or what radiation impact or atmospheric change might have been precipitated upon earth. Some scholars are loath to accept the solar-flare version of the moon glaze because of the stupendous energy which would have to be expended, and the general known stability of the sun. But men are short-lived, and solar catastrophes like the sunward disintegration of a comet would be exceedingly rare. Until more satisfactory evidence is at hand, most scientists will probably prefer to regard the glazed rock as splashed by the heat of meteoritic impact.

Nevertheless, the turbulent outpouring of even ordinary solar flares is on so gigantic a scale as to be terrifying in a close-up view. Until there is further evidence that ours is not a sleepy dragon star, one may wonder just what happened thirty thousand years ago, and why, among so many deaths, it was man who survived. Whatever occurred, whether by ice withdrawal or the momentary penetration of the ultraviolet into our atmosphere, man's world was changed. Perhaps there is something after all to the story of his eviction from the green Garden.

When I lie in bed now and await the hastening of Halley's comet, I would like to dream my way back just once to that single, precise instant when the star dragon thrust out its tongue. Perhaps the story of all dragons since comes from that moment. Men have long memories when the memories are clothed in myth. But I dream, and the train whistle mingles and howls with the heaven-sweeping light in my dream. It is 1910. I am going back once more.

The Star Dragon ✳ 27

TWO ❖ THE COSMIC PRISON

Not till we are lost . . . do we begin to understand ourselves.

—HENRY DAVID THOREAU

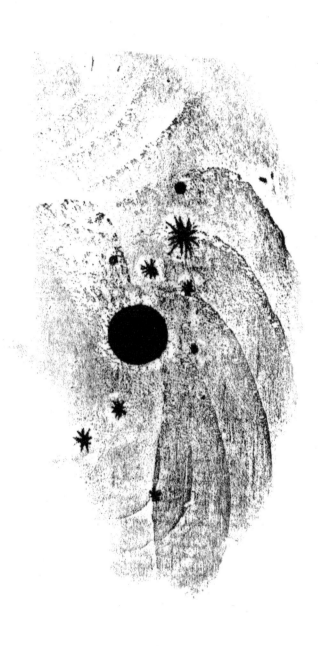

THE COSMIC PRISON

"A name is a prison, God is free," once observed the Greek poet Nikos Kazantzakis. He meant, I think, that valuable though language is to man, it is by very necessity limiting, and creates for man an invisible prison. Language implies boundaries. A word spoken creates a dog, a rabbit, a man. It fixes their nature before our eyes; henceforth their shapes are, in a sense, our own creation. They are no longer part of the unnamed shifting architecture of the universe. They have been transfixed as if by sorcery, frozen into a concept, a word. Powerful though the spell of human language has proven itself to be, it has laid boundaries upon the cosmos.

No matter how far-ranging some of the mental probes that man has philosophically devised, by his own created nature he is forced to hold the specious and emerging present and transform it into words. The words are startling in their immediate effectiveness, but at the same time they are always finally imprisoning because man has constituted himself a prison keeper. He does so out of no conscious intention, but because for immediate purposes he has created an unnatural world of his own, which he calls the cultural world, and in which he feels at home. It defines his needs and allows him to lay a small immobilizing spell upon the nearer portions of his universe. Nevertheless, it transforms that universe into a cosmic prison house which is no sooner mapped than man feels its inadequacy and his own.

He seeks then to escape, and the theory of escape involves bodily flight. Scarcely had the first moon landing been achieved before one U. S. senator boldly announced: "We are the masters of the universe. We can go anywhere we choose." This statement was widely and editorially acclaimed. It is a striking example of the comfort of words, also of the covert substitutions and mental projections to which they are subject. The cosmic prison is not made less so by a successful journey of some two hundred and forty thousand miles in a cramped and primitive vehicle.

To escape the cosmic prison man is poorly equipped. He has to drag portions of his environment with him, and his life span is that of a mayfly in terms of the distances he seeks to penetrate. There is no possible way to master such a universe by flight alone. Indeed such a dream is a dangerous illusion. This may seem a heretical statement, but its truth is self-evident if we try seriously to comprehend the nature of time and space that I sought to grasp when held up to view the fiery messenger that flared across the zenith in 1910. "Seventy-five years," my father had whispered in my ear, "seventy-five years and it will be racing homeward. Perhaps you will live to see it again. Try to remember."

And so I remembered. I had gained a faint glimpse of the size of our prison house. Somewhere out there beyond a billion miles in space, an entity known as a comet had rounded on its track in the black darkness of the void. It was surging homeward toward the sun because it was an eccentric satellite of this solar system. If I lived to see it it would be but barely, and with the dimmed eyes of age. Yet it, too, in its long traverse, was but a flitting mayfly in terms of the universe the night sky revealed.

So relative is the cosmos we inhabit that, as we gaze upon the outer galaxies available to the reach of our telescopes, we are placed in about the position that a single white blood cell in our bodies would occupy, if it were intelligently capable of seeking to understand the nature of its own universe, the body it inhabits. The cell would encounter rivers ramifying into miles of distance seemingly leading nowhere. It would pass through gigantic structures whose meaning it could never grasp—the brain, for example. It could never know there was an outside, a vast being on a scale it could not conceive of and of which it formed an infinitesimal part. It would know only the pouring tumult of the creation it inhabited, but of the nature of that great beast, or even indeed that it was a beast, it could have no conception whatever. It might examine the liquid in which it floated and decide, as in the case of the fall of Lucretius's atoms, that the pouring of obscure torrents had created its world.

It might discover that creatures other than itself swam in the torrent. But that its universe was alive, had been born and was destined to perish, its own ephemeral existence would never allow it to perceive. It would never know the sun; it would explore only through dim tactile sensations and react to chemical stimuli that were borne to it along the mysterious conduits of the arteries and veins. Its universe would be centered upon a great arborescent tree of spouting blood. This, at best, generations of white blood cells by enormous labor and continuity might succeed, like astronomers, in charting.

They could never, by any conceivable stretch of the imagination, be aware that their so-called universe was, in actuality, the prowling body of a cat or the more time-enduring body of a philosopher, himself engaged upon the same quest in a more gigantic world and perhaps deceived proportionately by greater vistas. What if, for example, the far galaxies man observes make up, across void spaces of which even we are atomically composed, some kind of enormous creature or cosmic snowflake whose exterior we will never see? We will know more than the phagocyte in our bodies, but no more than that limited creature can we climb out of our universe, or successfully enhance our size or longevity sufficiently to thrust our heads through the confines of the universe that terminates our vision.

Some further "outside" will hover elusively in our thought, but upon its nature, or even its reality, we can do no more than speculate. The phagocyte might observe the salty turbulence of an eternal river system, Lucretius the fall of atoms creating momentary living shapes. We suspiciously sense, in the concept of the expanding universe derived from the primordial atom—the monobloc—some kind of oscillating universal heart. At the instant of its contraction we will vanish. It is not given us, nor can our science recapture, the state beyond the monobloc, nor whether we exist in the diastole of some inconceivable being. We know only a little more extended reality than the hypothetical creature below us. Above us may lie realms it is beyond our power to grasp.

II

This, then, is the secret nature of the universe over which the ebullient senator so recklessly proclaimed our absolute mastery. Time in that universe is in excess of ten billion years. It recedes backward into a narrowing funnel where, at some inconceivable point of concentration, the monobloc containing all the matter that composes the galaxies exploded in the one gigantic instant of creation.

Along with that explosion space itself is rushing outward. Stars and the great island galaxies in which they cluster are more numerous than the blades of grass upon a plain. To speak of man as "mastering" such a cosmos is about the equivalent of installing a grasshopper as Secretary General of the United Nations. Worse, in fact, for no matter what system of propulsion man may invent in the future, the galaxies on the outer rim of visibility are fleeing faster than he can approach them. Moreover, the light that he is receiving from them left its source in the early history of the planet earth. There is no possible way of even establishing their present existence. As the British astronomer Sir Bernard Lovell has so appropriately remarked, "At the limit of present-day observations our information is a few billion years out of date."

Light travels at a little over one hundred and eighty-six thousand miles a second, far beyond the conceivable speed of any spaceship devised by man, yet it takes light something like one hundred thousand years just to travel across the star field of our own galaxy, the Milky Way. It has been estimated that to reach the nearest star to our own, four light-years away, would require, at the present speed of our spaceships, a time equivalent to more than the whole of written history, indeed one hundred thousand earthly years would be a closer estimate—a time as long, perhaps, as the whole existence of *Homo sapiens* upon earth. And the return, needless to state, would consume just as long a period.

Even if our present rocket speeds were stepped up by a factor of one hundred, human generations would pass on the voyage. An unmanned probe into the nearer galactic realms would be gone so long that its intended mission, in fact the country which sent it forth, might both have vanished into the mists of history before its messages began to be received. All this, be it noted, does not begin to involve us in those intergalactic distances across which a radio message from a cruising spaceship might take hundreds of years to be received and a wait of other hundreds before a reply would filter back.

We are, in other words, truly in the position of the blood cell exploring our body. We are limited in time, by analogy a miniature replica of the cosmos, since we too individually ascend from a primordial atom, exist, and grow in space, only to fall back in dissolution. We cannot, in terms of the time dimension as we presently know it, either travel or survive the interstellar distances.

Two years ago I chanced to wander with a group of visiting scholars into a small planetarium in a nearby city. In the dark in a remote back seat, I grew tired and fell asleep while a lecture was progressing. My eyes had closed upon a present-day starry night as represented in the northern latitudes. After what seemed in my uneasy slumber the passage of a long period of time, I started awake in the dark, my eyes fixed in amazement upon the star vault overhead. All was quiet in the neighboring high-backed seats. I could see no one. Suddenly I seemed adrift under a vast and unfamiliar sky. Constellations with which I was familiar had shifted, grown minute, or vanished. I rubbed my eyes. This was not the universe in which I had fallen asleep. It seemed more still, more remote, more enormous, and inconceivably more solitary. A queer sense of panic struck me, as though I had been transported out of time.

Only after some attempt to orient myself by a diminished pole star did the answer come to me by murmurs from without. I was not the last man on the planet, far in the dying future. My companions had arisen and left, while the lecturer had terminated his address by setting the planetarium lights forward to show the conformation of the heavens as they might exist in the remote future of the expanding universe. Distances had lengthened. All was poised, chill, and alone.

I sat for a moment experiencing the sensation all the more intensely because of the slumber which left me feeling as though ages had elapsed. The sky gave little sign of movement. It seemed drifting in a slow indeterminate swirl, as though the forces of expansion were equaled at last by some monstrous tug of gravity at the heart of things. In this remote night sky of the far future I felt myself waiting upon the inevitable, the great drama and surrender of the inward fall, the heart contraction of the cosmos.

I was still sitting when, like the slightest leaf movement on a flooding stream, I saw the first faint galaxy of a billion suns race like a silverfish across the night and vanish. It was enough: the fall was equal to the flash of creation. I had sensed it waiting there under the star vault of the planetarium. Now it was cascading like a torrent through the ages in my head. I had experienced, by chance, the farthest reach of the star prison. I had similarly lived to see the beginning descent into the maelstrom.

III

There are other confinements, however, than that imposed by the enormous distances of the cosmos. One could almost list them. There is, for example, the prison of smells. I happen to know a big black hunting poodle named Beau. Beau loves to go for walks in the woods, and at such times as I visit his owners this task of seeing Beau safely through his morning adventures is happily turned over to me.

Beau has eyes, of course, and I do not doubt that he uses them when he greets his human friends by proffering a little gift such as his food dish. After this formality, which dates to his puppyhood, is completed, Beau immediately reverts to the world of snuffles. As a long-time trusted friend, I have frequently tried to get Beau to thrust his head out of the world of smells and actually to see the universe. I have led him before the mirror in my bedroom and tried to persuade him to see himself, his own visible identity. The results, it turns out, are totally unsatisfactory if not ludicrous. Beau peers out from his black ringlets as suspiciously as an ape hiding in a bush. He drops his head immediately and pretends to examine the floor. It is evident that he detests this apparition and has no intention of being cajoled into some dangerous and undoggy wisdom by my voice.

He promptly brings his collar and makes appropriate throaty conversation. To appease his wounded feelings, I set out for a walk in the woods. It is necessary to do this with a long chain and a very tight grasp upon it. Beau is a big, powerful animal, and ringlets or no he has come from an active and carnivorous past. Once in the woods all this past suddenly emerges. One is dragged willy-nilly through leaf, thorn, and thicket on intangible trails that Beau's swinging muzzle senses upon the wind.

His deep, wet nose has entered a world denied to me— a mad world whose contours and direction change with every gust of air. I leap and bound with a chafed wrist through a smell universe I cannot even sense. Occasionally something squawks or bounds from under our feet and I am flung against trees or wrapped around by a flying chain.

Finally, on one memorable occasion, after a rain, Beau paused, sniffing suspiciously between two rocks on a hillside. Another rabbit? I groaned mentally, taking a tighter hold on the chain. Beau then began some careful digging, curving and patting the soil aside in a way I had never before witnessed. A small basin shaped by Beau's forepaws presently appeared, and up from the bottom of it welled a spring-fed pool in which Beau promptly buried his snout and lapped long and lustily of water that I am sure carried the living tastes and delicate nuances disseminated from an unseen watershed.

Beau had had a proper drink of tap water before we started from home, but this drink was different. I could tell from the varied, eager, slurping sounds that emanated

The Cosmic Prison ✦ 39

from Beau. He was intoxicated by living water which dim primordial memories had instructed him how to secure. I looked on, interested and sympathetic, but aware that the big black animal lived in a smell prison as I, in my way, lived in a sight prison. Our universes intersected sufficiently for us to recognize each other in a friendly fashion, but Beau would never admit the mirror image of himself into his mind, and, try as I would, the passing breeze would never inform me about the shadowy creatures that passed unglimpsed in the forest.

IV

Other prisons exist besides those dominated by the senses of smell or sight or temperature. Some involve the length of a creature's lifetime, as in the case of five-year-old Beau, who gambols happily about his master, knowing him to be one of the everlasting immortals of his universe.

It is my belief that there has never been a culture that represented man any more than there has been a man who represented men. Our prisons, both societal and cultural, are far too complex for this. In one age religion drives the scientist-philosopher into hiding in narrow corners or castigates him as a public enemy. Such was the fate of Nicolaus Copernicus, Galileo Galilei, and others of equal importance. The pharaohs, by contrast, dreamed of traversing the sky after death in solar boats which they prepared after the fashion of Mediterranean sea craft. The Old Kingdom pharaohs, however, were entranced by a pole-star conception of their final voyage. Only later did the solar journey take precedence. I mention these cultural prisons only to indicate that man's cosmic yearnings are very old but subjected to the vicissitudes of history.

The dream of men elsewhere in the universe alleviating the final prison of loneliness dies very hard. Nevertheless a wise remark of George Santayana's made many years ago should discourage facile and optimistic thinking upon this very point. "An infinite number of solar systems," the philosopher meditated, "must have begun as ours began, but each of them must have deviated at one point from ours in its evolution, all the previous incidents being followed in each case by a different sequel." In voicing this view Santayana betrays a clearer concept of the chance-filled course of genetics and its unreturning pathways than some astronomers. The Mendelian pathways are prisons of no return. Advances are made but always a door swings shut behind the evolving organism. It can no longer mate with its one-time progenitors. It can only press forward along roads that increasingly will fix its irrevocable destiny.

Ours is a man-centered age. Not long ago I was perusing a work on space when I came across this statement by a professional astronomer: "Other stars, other planets, other life, and other races of men are evolving all along, so that the net effect is changeless." Implied in this remark was an utter confidence that the evolutionary process was everywhere the same, ran through the same succession of forms, and emerged always with men at the helm of life, men presumably so close to ourselves that they might interbreed—a supposition fostered by our comic strips.

In the light of this naive concept, for such it is, let us consider just two worlds we know about, not worlds in space, but continents on our own planet. These continents exist under the same sun and are surrounded by the same waters as our own; their life bears a distant relationship to ours but has long been isolated. Man never arose in the remote regions of South America and Australia. He only reached them by migration from outside. They are laboratories of agelong evolution which tell us much about the unique quality of the human experience.

The southern continents of our earth do not maintain the intimacy of faunal exchange that marks the land masses encircling the basin of the polar sea. Instead, they are lost in the southern latitudes of the oceans and for long intervals their faunas have evolved in isolation. These lands have been in truth "other worlds."

The most isolated of these worlds is Australia, and it is a marsupial world. With the insignificant exception of a few late drifters from outside, ground life, originally represented by a few marsupial forms, has, since the Mesozoic, evolved untroubled by invading placental mammals from without. Every possible ecological niche from forest tree to that of underground burrower has been occupied by the evolutionary radiation of a slower-brained mammal whose young are born in a far more embryonic condition than are those of the true Placentalia.

This world remained unknown to Western science until the great exploratory voyages. Somewhere in the past, life had taken another turn. Chance mutation, "total contingency" in the words of the paleontologist William King Gregory, had led to another universe. The "world" of Australia contained no primates at all, nor any hint of their emergence. Upon that "planet" lost in the great waters, they were one of an infinite number of random potentialities that had remained as unrealized as the whole group of placental mammals, of which the Primate order is a minor part.

If we now turn to South America, we encounter still another isolated evolutionary center—but one not totally unrelated to that of Eurasia. Here, so the biogeographers inform us, an attenuated land bridge, at intervals completely severed, has both stimulated local evolutionary development and at times interrupted it by migrations from North America. Our concern is with just one group of animals, the South American monkeys. They are anatomically distinct from the catarrhine forms of the Old World and constitute an apparent parallel emergence from the prosimians of the early Tertiary.

Once more, however, even though the same basic Primate stock is involved, things have gone differently. There are no great apes in the New World, no evidence of ground-dwelling experiments of any kind. Though fewer carnivores are to be found on the South American grasslands than in Africa, the rain-forest monkeys, effectively equipped with prehensile tails, still cling to their archaic pathways. One can only observe that South America's vast rivers flow through frequently flooded lowlands, and that by contrast much of Africa is high, with open savannah and parkland. The South American primates appear confined to areas where descent to the ground proved less inviting. Here ended another experiment which did not lead to man, even though it originated within the same order from which he sprang. Another world has gone astray from the human direction.

If, as some thinkers occasionally extrapolate, man was so ubiquitous, so easy to produce, why had two great continental laboratories, Australia and South America—

"worlds," indeed—failed to produce him? They had failed, we may assume, simply because the great movements of life are irreversible, the same mutations do not occur, circumstances differ in infinite particulars, opportunities fail to be grasped, and so what once happened is no more. The random element is always present, but it is selected on the basis of what has preceded its appearance.

There is no trend demanding man's constant reappearance, either on the separate "worlds" of this earth or elsewhere. There can be no more random duplication of man than there is a random duplication of such a complex genetic phenomenon as fingerprints. The situation is not one that is comparable to a single identical cast of dice, but rather it is an endless addition of new genes building on what has previously been incorporated into a living creature through long ages. Nature gambles but she gambles with constantly new and altering dice. It is this well-established fact which enables us to call long-range evolution irreversible.

Finally, there are even meteorological prisons. The constant circulation of moisture in our atmosphere has actually played an important role in creating the first vertebrates and, indirectly, man. If early rivers had not poured from the continents into the sea, the first sea vertebrates to penetrate streams above sea level would not have evolved a rigid muscular support, the spine, to enable them to wriggle against down-rushing currents. And, if man, in his early history, had not become a tree climber in tropical rain forests, he would never have further tilted that same spine upright or replaced the smell prison of the horizontal mammal with the stereoscopic, far-ranging "eye brain" of the higher primates, including man. Such final dice throws, in which leaf and grass, wave and water, are inextricably commingled with the chemistry of the body, could be multiplied. The cosmic prison is subdivided into an infinite number of unduplicable smaller prisons, the prisons of form.

V

We are now in a position to grasp, after an examination of the many prisons which encompass life, that the cosmic prison which many men, in the excitement of the first moon landing, believed we had escaped still extends immeasurably beyond us. The present lack of any conceivable means of star travel and the shortness of our individual lives appear to prevent the crossing of such distances. Even if we confined ourselves to unmanned space probes of far greater sophistication than any we now possess, their homing messages through the void could be expected to descend upon the ruined radio scanners of a civilization long vanished, or upon a world whose scholars would have long since forgotten what naive dreams had been programmed into such instruments. We have, in other words, detected that we exist in a prison of numbers, otherwise known as light-years. We are also locked in a body which responds to biological rather than sidereal time. That body, in turn, sees the universe through its own senses and no others.

At every turn of thought a lock snaps shut upon us. As societal men we bow to a given frame of culture—a world view we have received from the past. Biologically each of us is unique, and the tight spiral of the DNA molecules conspires to doom us to mediocrity or grandeur. We dream vast dreams of Utopias and live to learn the meaning of the two-thousand-year-old judgment of a Greek philosopher: "The flaw is in the vessel itself "— the flaw that defeats all governments.

By what means, then, can we seek escape from groveling in mean corners of despair? Not, certainly, by the rush to depart upon the night's black pathways, nor by attention to the swerving wind vane of the senses. We are men, and despite all our follies there have been great ones among us who have counseled us in wisdom, men who have also sought keys to our prison. Strangely, these men have never spoken of space; they have spoken, instead, as though the farthest spaces lay within the mind itself—as though we still carried a memory of some light of long ago and the way we had come. Perhaps for this reason alone we have scanned the skies and the waters with what Henry Vaughan so well labeled the "Ecclips'd Eye," that eye incapable of quite assembling the true meaning of the universe but striving to do so "with Hyeroglyphicks quite dismembered."

These are the words of a seventeenth-century mystic who has mentally dispatched inward vision through all the creatures until he comes to man who "shines a little" and whose depths he finds it impossible to plumb. Thomas Traherne, another man of that century of the Ecclips'd Eye, when religion was groping amidst the revelations of science, stated well the matter of the keys to the prison.

"Infinite love," he ventured, "cannot be expressed in finite room. Yet it must be infinitely expressed in the smallest moment, . . .Only so is it in both ways infinite."

Can this insight be seen to justify itself in modern evolutionary terms? I think it can.

Close to a hundred years ago the great French medical scientist Claude Bernard observed that the stability of the inside environment of complex organisms must be maintained before an outer freedom can be achieved from their immediate surroundings. What Bernard meant was profound but simple to illustrate.

He meant that for life to obtain relative security from its fickle and dangerous outside surroundings the animal must be able to sustain stable, unchanging conditions within the body. Warm-blooded mammals and birds can continue to move about in winter; insects cannot. Warm-blooded animals such as man, with his stable body temperature, can continue to think and reason in outside temperatures that would put a frog to sleep in a muddy pond or roll a snake into a ball in a crevice. In winter latitudes many of the lower creatures are forced to sleep part of their lives away.

Many millions of years of evolutionary effort were required before life was successful in defending its internal world from the intrusion of the heat or cold of the outside world of nature. Yet only so can life avoid running down like a clock in winter or perishing from exposure in the midday sun. Even the desert rattlesnake is forced to coil in the shade of a bush at midday. Of course our tolerance is limited to a few degrees of temperature when measured against the great thermometer of the stars, but this hard-won victory is what creates the ever-active brain of the mammal as against the retarded sluggishness of the reptile.

A steady metabolism has enabled the mammals and also the birds to experience life more fully and rapidly than cold-blooded creatures. One of the great feats of evolution, perhaps the greatest, has been this triumph of the interior environment over exterior nature. Inside, we might say, has fought invading outside, and inside, since the beginning of life, by slow degrees has won the battle of life. If it had not, man, frail man with his even more fragile brain, would not exist.

Unless fever or some other disorder disrupts this internal island of safety, we rarely think of it. Body controls are normally automatic, but let them once go wrong and outside destroys inside. This is the simplest expression of the war of nature—the endless conflict that engages the microcosm against the macrocosm.

Since the first cell created a film about itself and elected to carry on the carefully insulated processes known as life, the creative spark has not been generalized. Whatever its principle may be it hides magically within individual skins. To the day of our deaths we exist in an inner solitude that is linked to the nature of life itself. Even as we project love and affection upon others we endure a loneliness which is the price of all individual consciousness—the price of living.

It is, though overlooked, the discontinuity beyond all others: the separation both of the living creature from the inanimate and of the individual from his kind. These are star distances. In man, moreover, consciousness looks out isolated from its own body. The body is the true cosmic prison, yet it contains, in the creative individual, a magnificent if sometimes helpless giant. John Donne, speaking for that giant in each of us, said: "Our creatures are our thoughts, creatures that are borne Gyants. . . . My thoughts reach all, comprehend all. Inexplicable mystery; I their

Creator am in a close prison, in a sick bed, anywhere, and any one of my Creatures, my thoughts, is with the Sunne and beyond the Sunne, overtakes the Sunne, and overgoes the Sunne in one pace, one steppe, everywhere."

This thought, expressed so movingly by Donne, represents the final triumph of Claude Bernard's interior microcosm in its war with the macrocosm. Inside has conquered outside. The giant confined in the body's prison roams at will among the stars. More rarely and more beautifully, perhaps, the profound mind in the close prison projects infinite love in a finite room. This is a crossing beside which light-years are meaningless. It is the solitary key to the prison that is man.

THREE ✤ THE WORLD EATERS

Really we create nothing. We merely plagiarize nature.

—JEAN BAITAILLON

THE WORLD EATERS

It came to me in the night, in the midst of a bad dream, that perhaps man, like the blight descending on a fruit, is by nature a parasite, a spore bearer, a world eater. The slime molds are the only creatures on the planet that share the ways of man from his individual pioneer phase to his final immersion in great cities. Under the microscope one can see the mold amoebas streaming to their meeting places, and no one would call them human. Nevertheless, magnified many thousand times and observed from the air, their habits would appear close to our own. This is because, when their microscopic frontier is gone, as it quickly is, the single amoeboid frontiersmen swarm into concentrated aggregations. At the last they thrust up overtoppling spore palaces, like city skyscrapers. The rupture of these vesicles may disseminate the living spores as far away proportionately as man's journey to the moon.

It is conceivable that in principle man's motor throughways resemble the slime trails along which are drawn the gathering mucors that erect the spore palaces, that man's cities are only the ephemeral moment of his spawning— that he must descend upon the orchard of far worlds or die.

Human beings are a strange variant in nature and a very recent one. Perhaps man has evolved as a creature whose centrifugal tendencies are intended to drive it as a blight is lifted and driven, outward across the night.

I do not believe, for reasons I will venture upon later, that this necessity is written in the genes of men, but it would be foolish not to consider the possibility, for man as an interplanetary spore bearer may be only at the first moment of maturation. After all, *Mucoroides* and its relatives must once have performed their act of dissemination for the very first time. In man, even if the feat is cultural, it is still possible that some incalculable and ancient urge lies hidden beneath the seeming rationality of institutionalized science. For example, a young space engineer once passionately exclaimed to me, "We must give all we have . . ." It was as though he were hypnotically compelled by that obscure chemical, acrasin, that draws the slime molds to their destiny. And is it not true also that observers like myself are occasionally bitterly castigated for daring to examine the motivation of our efforts toward space? In the intellectual climate of today one should strive to remember the words that Herman Melville accorded his proud, fate-confronting Captain Ahab, "All my means are sane, my motive and my object mad."

The cycles of parasites are often diabolically ingenious. It is to the unwilling host that their ends appear mad. Has earth hosted a new disease—that of the world eaters? Then inevitably the spores must fly. Short-lived as they are, they must fly. Somewhere far outward in the dark, instinct may intuitively inform them, lies the garden of the worlds. We must consider the possibility that we do not know the real nature of our kind. Perhaps *Homo sapiens*, the wise, is himself only a mechanism in a parasitic cycle, an instrument for the transference, ultimately, of a more invulnerable and heartless version of himself.

Or, again, the dark may bring him wisdom.

I stand in doubt as my forebears must once have done at the edge of the shrinking forest. I am a man of the rocket century; my knowledge, such as it is, concerns our past, our dubious present, and our possible future. I doubt our motives, but I grant us the benefit of the doubt and, like Arthur Clarke, call it, for want of a better term, "childhood's end." I also know, as did Plato, that one who has spent his life in the shadow of great wars may, like a captive, blink and be momentarily blinded when released into the light.

There are aspects of the world and its inhabitants that are eternal, like the ripples marked in stone on fossil beaches. There is a biological preordination that no one can change. These are seriatim events that only the complete reversal of time could undo. An example would be the moment when the bats dropped into the air and fluttered away from the insectivore line that gave rise to ourselves. What fragment of man, perhaps a useful fragment, departed with them? Something, shall we say, that had it lingered, might have made a small, brave, twilight difference in the mind of man.

There is a part of human destiny that is not fixed irrevocably but is subject to the flying shuttles of chance and will. Everyone imagines that he knows what is possible and what is impossible, but the whole of time and history attest our ignorance. One evening, in a drab and heartless area of the metropolis, a windborne milkweed seed circled my head. On impulse I seized the delicate aerial orphan which

The World Eaters * 55

otherwise would have perished. Its long midwinter voyage seemed too favorable an augury to ignore. Placing the seed in my glove, I took it home into the suburbs and found a field in which to plant it. Of a million seeds blown on a vagrant wind into the city, it alone may survive.

Why did I bother? I suppose, in retrospect, for the sake of the future and the memory of the bats whirling like departing thoughts from the tree of ancestral man. Perhaps, after all, there lingered in my reflexes enough of a voyager to help all travelers on the great highway of the winds. Or perhaps I am not yet totally a planet eater and wished that something green might survive. A single impulse, a hand outstretched to an alighting seed, suggests that something is still undetermined in the human psyche, that the time trap has not yet closed inexorably. Some aspect of man that has come with him from the sunlit grasses is still instinctively alive and being fought for. The future, formidable as a thundercloud, is still inchoate and unfixed upon the horizon.

II

Man is "a tinkerer playing with ideas and mechanisms," comments a recent and very able writer upon technology, R. J. Forbes. He goes on to state that, if those impulses were to disappear, man would cease to be a human being in the sense we know. It is necessary to concede to Forbes that for Western man, *Homo faber*, the tool user, the definition is indeed appropriate. Nevertheless, when we turn to the people of the wilderness we must place certain limitations upon the words. That man has utilized tools throughout his history is true, but that man has been particularly inventive or a tinkerer in the sense of seeking constant innovation is open to question.

Students of living primitives in backward areas such as Australia have found them addicted to immemorial usage in both ideas and tools. There is frequently a prejudice against the kind of change to which our own society has only recently adjusted. Such behavior is viewed askance as disruptive. The society is in marked ecological balance with its surroundings, and any drastic innovation from within the group is apt to be rejected as interfering with the will of the divine ancestors.

Not many years ago I fell to chatting with a naturalist who had had a long experience among the Cree of the northern forests. What had struck him about these Indians, even after considerable exposure to white men, was their remarkable and yet, in our terms, "indifferent" adjustment to their woodland environment. By indifference my informant meant that while totally skilled in the use of everything in their surroundings, they had little interest in experiment in a scientific sense, or in carrying objects about with them. Indeed they were frequently very careless with equipment or clothing given or loaned to them. Such things might be discarded after use or left hanging casually on a branch. One was left with the impression that these woodsmen were, by our standards, casual and feckless. Their reliance upon their own powers was great, but it was based on long traditional accommodation and a psychology by no means attuned to the civilized innovators' world. Plant fibers had their uses, wood had its uses, but everything from birch bark to porcupine quills was simply "given." Raw materials were always at hand, to be ignored or picked up as occasion demanded.

One carried little, one survived on little, and little in the way of an acquisitive society existed. One lived amidst all one had use for. If one shifted position in space the same materials were again present to be used. These people were ignorant of what Forbes would regard as the technological necessity to advance. Until the intrusion of whites, their technology had been long frozen upon a barely adequate subsistence level. "Progress" in Western terms was an unknown word.

Similarly I have heard the late Frank Speck discuss the failure of the Montagnais-Naskapi of the Labrador peninsula to take advantage, in their winter forest, either of Eskimo snow goggles, for which they substituted a mere sprig of balsam thrust under the cap, or of the snow house, which is far more comfortable than their cold and draft-exposed wigwams. The same indifference toward technological improvement or the acceptance of innovations from outside thus extended even to their racial brothers, the Eskimo. Man is a tool user, certainly, whether of the stone knife or less visible hunting magic. But that he is an obsessive innovator is far less clear. Tradition rules in the world's outlands. Man is not on this level driven to be inventive. Instead he is using the sum total of his environment almost as a single tool.

There is a very subtle point at issue here. H. C. Conklin, for example, writes about one Philippine people, the Hanunóo, that their "activities require an intimate familiarity with local plants . . . . Contrary to the assumption that subsistence level groups never use but a small segment of the local flora, ninety-three percent of the total number of native plant types are recognized . . . as culturally significant." As Claude Lévi-Strauss has been at pains to point out, this state of affairs has been observed in many simple cultures.

Scores of terms exist for objects in the natural environment for which civilized man has no equivalents at all. The latter is engaged primarily with his deepening shell of technology which either exploits the natural world or thrusts it aside. By contrast, man in the earlier cultures was so oriented that the total natural environment occupied his exclusive attention. If parts of it did not really help him practically, they were often inserted into magical patterns that did. Thus man existed primarily in a carefully reorganized nature—one that was watched, brooded over, and managed by magico-religious as well as practical means.

Nature was actually as well read as an alphabet; it was the real "tool" by which man survived with a paucity of practical equipment. Or one could say that the tool had largely been forged in the human imagination. It consisted of the way man had come to organize and relate himself to the sum total of his environment. This world view was comparatively static. Nature was sacred and contained powers which demanded careful propitiation. Modern man, on the other hand, has come to look upon nature as a thing outside himself—an object to be manipulated or discarded at will. It is his technology and its vocabulary that makes his primary world. If, like the primitive, he has a sacred center, it is here. Whatever is potential must be unrolled, brought into being at any cost. No other course is conceived as possible. The economic system demands it.

Two ways of life are thus arrayed in final opposition. One way reads deep, if sometimes mistaken, analogies into nature and maintains toward change a reluctant conservatism. The other is fiercely analytical. Having consciously discovered sequence and novelty, man comes to transfer the operation of the world machine to human hands and to install change itself as progress. A reconciliation of the two views would seem to be necessary if humanity is to survive. The obstacles, however, are great.

Nowhere are they better illustrated than in the decades-old story of an anthropologist who sought to contact a wild and untouched group of aborigines in the red desert of central Australia. Traveling in a truck loaded with water and simple gifts, the scientist finally located his people some five hundred miles from the nearest white settlement. The anthropologist lived with the bush folk for a few weeks and won their confidence. They trusted him. The time came to leave. Straight over the desert ran the the tracks of his car, and the aborigines are magnificent trackers.

Things were not the same when their friend had left; something had been transposed or altered in their landscape. The gifts had come so innocently. The little band set out one morning to follow the receding track of their friend. They were many days drifting on the march, drawn on perhaps by that dim impulse to which the slime molds yield. Eventually they came to the white man's frontier town. Their friend was gone, but there were other and less kindly white men. There were also drink, prostitution, and disease, about which they were destined to learn. They would never go back to the dunes and the secret places. In five years a begging and degraded remnant would stray through the outskirts of the settlers' town.

They had learned to their cost that it is possible to wander out of the world of the ancestors, only to become an object of scorn in a world directed to a different set of principles for which the aborigines had no guiding precedent. By leaving the timeless land they had descended into hell. Not all the tiny beings of the slime mold escape to new pastures; some wander, some are sacrificed to make the spore cities, and but a modicum of the original colony mounts the winds of space. It is so in the cities of men.

III

Over a century ago Samuel Taylor Coleridge ruminated in one of his own encounters with the universe that "A Fall of some sort or other—the creation as it were of the non-absolute—is the fundamental postulate of the moral history of man. Without this hypothesis, man is unintelligible; with it every phenomenon is explicable. The mystery itself is too profound for human insight."

In making this observation Coleridge had come very close upon the flaw that was to create, out of a comparatively simple creature, the world eaters of the twentieth century. How, is a mystery to be explored, because every man on the planet belongs to the same species, and every man communicates. A span of three centuries has been enough to produce a planetary virus, while on that same planet a few lost tribesmen with brains the biological equal of our own peer in astonishment from the edges of the last wilderness.

One of the scholars of the scientific twilight, Joseph Glanvill, was quick to intimate that to posterity a voyage to the moon "will not be more strange than one to America." Even in 1665 the ambitions of the present century had entered human consciousness. The paradox is already present. There is the man *Homo sapiens* who in various obscure places around the world would rarely think of altering the simple tools of his forefathers, and, again, there is this same *Homo sapiens* in a wild flurry of modern thought patterns reversing everything by which he had previously lived. Such an episode parallels the rise of a biological mutation as potentially virulent in its effects as a new bacterial strain. The fact that its nature appears to be cultural merely enables the disease to be spread with fantastic rapidity. There is no comparable episode in history.

There are two things which are basic to an understanding of the way in which the primordial people differ from the world eaters, ourselves. Coleridge was quite right that man no more than any other living creature represented the absolute. He was finite and limited, and thus his ability to wreak his will upon the world was limited. He might dream of omniscient power, he might practice magic to obtain it, but such power remained beyond his grasp.

As a primitive, man could never do more than linger at the threshold of the energy that flickered in his campfire, nor could he hurl himself beyond Pluto's realm of frost. He was still within nature. True, he had restructured the green world in his mind so that it lay slightly ensorceled under the noonday sun. Nevertheless the lightning still roved and struck at will; the cobra could raise its deathly hood in the peasant's hut at midnight. The dark was thronged with spirits.

Man's powerful, undisciplined imagination had created a region beyond the visible spectrum which would sometimes aid and sometimes destroy him. Its propitiation and control would occupy and bemuse his mind for long millennia. To climb the fiery ladder that the spore bearers have used one must consume the resources of a world. Since such resources are not to be tapped without the drastic reordering of man's mental world, his final feat has as its first preliminary the invention of a way to pass knowledge through the doorway of the tomb—namely, the achievement of the written word.

Only so can knowledge be made sufficiently cumulative to challenge the stars. Our brothers of the forest have not lived in the world we have entered. They do not possess the tiny figures by which the dead can be made to speak from those great cemeteries of thought known as libraries. Man's first giant step for mankind was not through space. Instead it lay through time. Once more in the words of Glanvill, "That men should speak after their tongues were ashes, or communicate with each other in differing Hemisphears, before the Invention of Letters could not but have been thought a fiction."

In the first of the world's cities man had begun to live against the enormous backdrop of the theatre. He had become self-conscious, a man enacting his destiny before posterity. As ruler, conqueror, or thinker he lived, as Lewis Mumford has put it, by and for the record. In such a life both evil and good come to cast long shadows into the future. Evil leads to evil, good to good, but frequently the former is the most easy for the cruel to emulate. Moreover, when invention lends itself to centralized control, the individualism of the early frontiers easily gives way to routinized conformity. If life is made easier it is also made more dependent. If artificial demands are stimulated, resources must be consumed at an ever-increasing pace.

As in the microscopic instance of the slime molds, the

movement into the urban aggregations is intensified. The most technically advanced peoples will naturally consume the lion's share of the earth's resources. Thus the United States at present, representing some six percent of the world's population, consumes over thirty-four percent of its energy and twenty-nine percent of its steel. Over a billion pounds of trash are spewed over the landscape in a single year. In these few elementary facts, which are capable of endless multiplication, one can see the shape of the future growing—the future of a planet virus *Homo sapiens* as he assumes in his technological phase what threatens to be his final role.

Experts have been at pains to point out that the accessible crust of the earth is finite, while the demand for minerals steadily increases as more and more societies seek for themselves a higher, Westernized standard of living. Unfortunately many of these sought-after minerals are not renewable, yet a viable industrial economy demands their steady output. A rising world population requiring an improved standard of living clashes with the oncoming realities of a planet of impoverished resources.

"We live in an epoch of localized affluence," asserts Thomas Lovering, an expert on mineral resources. A few shifts and subterfuges may, with increasing effort and expense, prolong this affluence, but no feat of scientific legerdemain can prevent the eventual exhaustion of the world's mineral resources at a time not very distant. It is thus apparent that to apply to Western industrial man the term "world eater" is to do so neither in derision nor contempt. We are facing, instead, a simple reality to which, up until recently, the only response has been flight—the flight outward from what appears unsolvable and which threatens,

in the end, to leave an impoverished human remnant cling-
ing to an equally impoverished globe.

So quick and so insidious has been the rise of the world
virus that its impact is just beginning to be felt and its
history to be studied. Basically man's planetary virulence
can be ascribed to just one thing: a rapid ascent, particularly in the last three centuries, of an energy ladder so great
that the line on the chart repesenting it would be almost
vertical. The event, in the beginning, involved only Western European civilization. Today it increasingly character-
izes most of the planet.

The earliest phase of the human acquisition of energy
beyond the needs of survival revolves, as observed earlier,
around the rise of the first agricultural civilizations shortly
after the close of the Ice Age. Only with the appearance
of wealth in the shape of storable grains can the differentia-
tion of labor and of social classes, as well as an increase in
population, lay the basis for the expansion of the urban
world. With this event the expansion of trade and trade
routes was sure to follow. The domestication of plants and
animals, however, was still an event of the green world and
the sheepfold. Nevertheless it opened a doorway in nature
that had lain concealed from man.

Like all earth's other creatures, he had previously existed in a precarious balance with nature. In spite of his
adaptability, man, the hunter, had spread across the continents like thin fire burning over a meadow. It was impossible for his numbers to grow in any one place, because man,
multiplying, quickly consumes the wild things upon
which he feeds and then himself faces starvation. Only
with plant domestication is the storage granary made possible and through it three primary changes in the life of

man: a spectacular increase in human numbers; diversification of labor; the ability to feed from the countryside the spore cities into which man would presently stream.

After some four million years of lingering in nature's shadow, man would appear to have initiated a drastic change in the world of the animal gods and the magic that had seen him through millennial seasons. Such a change did not happen overnight, and we may never learn the details of its incipient beginnings. As we have already noted, at the close of the Ice Age, and particularly throughout the northern hemisphere, the big game, the hairy mammoth and mastodon, the giant long-horned bison, had streamed away with the melting glaciers. Sand was blowing over the fertile plains of North Africa and the Middle East. Gloomy forests were springing up in the Europe of the tundra hunters. The reindeer and musk ox had withdrawn far into the north on the heels of the retreating ice.

Man must have turned, in something approaching agony and humiliation, to the women with their digging sticks and arcane knowledge of seeds. Slowly, with greater ceremonial, the spring and harvest festivals began to replace the memory of the "gods with the wet nose," the bison gods of the earlier free-roving years. Whether for good or ill the world would never be the same. The stars would no longer be the stars of the wandering hunters. Halley's comet returning would no longer gleam on the tossing antlers and snowy backs of the moving game herds. Instead it would glimmer from the desolate tarns left by the ice in dark forests or startle shepherds watching flocks on the stony hills of Judea. Perhaps it was the fleeting star seen by the three wise men of legend, for a time of human transcendence was approaching.

To comprehend the rise of the world eaters one must leap centuries and millennia. To account for the rise of high-energy civilization is as difficult as to explain the circumstances that have gone into the creation of man himself. Certainly the old sun-plant civilizations provided leisure for meditation, mathematics, and transport energy through the use of sails. Writing, which arose among them, created a kind of stored thought-energy, an enhanced social brain.

All this the seed-and-sun world contributed, but no more. Not all of these civilizations left the traditional religious round of the seasons or the worship of the sun-kings installed on earth. Only far on in time, in west Europe, did a new culture and a new world emerge. Perhaps it would be best to limit our exposition to one spokesman who immediately anticipated its appearance. "If we must select some one philosopher as the hero of the revolution in scientific method," maintained William Whewell, the nineteenth-century historian, "beyond all doubt Francis Bacon occupies the place of honor." This view is based upon four simple precepts, the first of which, from *The Advancement of Learning*, I will give in Bacon's own words. "As the foundation," he wrote, "we are not to imagine or suppose, but to *discover* what nature does or may be made to do." Today this sounds like a truism. In Bacon's time it was a novel, analytical, and unheard-of way to explore nature. Bacon was thus the herald of what has been called "the invention of inventions"—the scientific method itself.

He believed also that the thinker could join with the skilled worker—what we today would call the technologist —to conduct experiment more ably than by simple and untested meditation in the cloister. Bacon, in other words, was groping toward the idea of the laboratory, of a whole new way of schooling. Within such schools, aided by government support, he hoped for the solution of problems not to be dealt with "in the hourglass of one man's life." In expressing this hope he had recognized that great achievement in science must not wait on the unaided and rare genius, but that research should be institutionalized and supported over the human generations.

Fourth and last of Bacon's insights was his vision of the future to be created by science. Here there clearly emerges that orientation toward the future which has since preoccupied the world of science and the West. Bacon was preeminently the spokesman of *anticipatory* man. The long reign of the custom-bound scholastics was at an end. Anticipatory analytical man, enraptured by novelty, was about to walk an increasingly dangerous pathway.

He would triumph over disease and his numbers would mount; steam and, later, air transport would link the ends of the earth. Agriculture would fall under scientific management, and fewer men on the land would easily support the febrile millions in the gathering cities. As Glanvill had foreseen, thought would fly upon the air. Man's telescopic eye would rove through the galaxy and beyond. No longer would men be burned or tortured for dreaming of life on far-off worlds.

There came, too, in the twentieth century to mock the dream of progress the most ruthless and cruel wars of history. They were the first wars fought with total scientific detachment. Cities were fire-bombed, submarines turned the night waters into a flaming horror, the air was black with opposing air fleets.

The laboratories of Bacon's vision produced the atom

bomb and toyed prospectively with deadly nerve gas. "Overkill" became a professional word. Iron, steel, Plexiglas, and the deadly mathematics of missile and anti-missile occupied the finest constructive minds. Even before space was entered, man began to assume the fixed mask of the robot. His courage was unbreakable, but in society there was mounting evidence of strain. Billions of dollars were being devoured in the space effort, while at the same time an affluent civilization was consuming its resources at an ever-increasing rate. Air and water and the land itself were being polluted by the activities of a creature grown used to the careless ravage of a continent.

Francis Bacon had spoken one further word on the subject of science, but by the time that science came its prophet had been forgotten. He had spoken of learning as intended to bring an enlightened life. Western man's ethic is not directed toward the preservation of the earth that fathered him. A devouring frenzy is mounting as his numbers mount. It is like the final movement in the spore palaces of the slime molds. Man is now only a creature of anticipation feeding upon events.

"When evil comes it is because two gods have disagreed," runs the proverb of an elder people. Perhaps it is another way of saying that the past and the future are at war in the heart of man. On March 7, 1970, as I sit at my desk the eastern seaboard is swept by the shadow of the greatest eclipse since 1900. Beyond my window I can see a strangely darkened sky, as though the light of the sun were going out forever. For an instant, lost in the dim gray light, I experience an equally gray clarity of vision.

IV

There is a tradition among the little Bushmen of the Kalahari desert that eclipses of the moon are caused by Kingsfoot, the lion who covers the moon's face with his paw to make the night dark for hunting. Since our most modern science informs us we have come from animals, and since almost all primitives have tended to draw their creator gods from the animal world with which they were familiar, modern man and his bush contemporaries have arrived at the same conclusion by very different routes. Both know that they are shape shifters and changelings. They know their relationship to animals by different ways of logic and different measures of time.

Modern man, the world eater, respects no space and no thing green or furred as sacred. The march of the machines has entered his blood. They are his seed boxes, his potential wings and guidance systems on the far roads of the universe. The fruition time of the planet virus is at hand. It is high autumn, the autumn before winter topples the spore cities. "The living memory of the city disappears," writes Mumford of this phase of urban life; "its inhabitants live in a self-annihilating moment to moment continuum." The ancestral center exists no longer. Anonymous millions roam the streets.

On the African veldt the lion, the last of the great carnivores, is addressed by the Bushmen over a kill whose ownership is contested. They speak softly the age-old ritual words for the occasion, "Great Lions, Old Lions, we know that you are brave." Nevertheless the little, almost weaponless people steadily advance. The beginning and the end are dying in unison and the one is braver than the other. Dreaming on by the eclipse-darkened window, I know with a sudden sure premonition that Kingsfoot has put his paw once more against the moon. The animal gods will come out for one last hunt.

Beginning on some winter night the snow will fall steadily for a thousand years and hush in its falling the spore cities whose seed has flown. The delicate traceries of the frost will slowly dim the glass in the observatories and all will be as it had been before the virus wakened. The long trail of Halley's comet, once more returning, will pass like a ghostly matchflame over the unwatched grave of the cities. This has always been their end, whether in the snow or in the sand.

FOUR ❖ THE SPORE BEARERS

Either the machine has a meaning to life that we have not yet been able to interpret in a rational manner, or it is itself a manifestation of life and therefore mysterious.

—GARET GARRETT

THE SPORE BEARERS

It is a remarkable fact that much of what man has achieved through the use of his intellect, nature had invented before him. *Pilobolus*, another fungus which prepares, sights, and fires its spore capsule, constitutes a curious anticipation of human rocketry. The fungus is one that grows upon the dung of cattle. To fulfill its life cycle, its spores must be driven up and outward to land upon vegetation several feet away, where they may be eaten by grazing cows or horses.

The spore tower that discharges the *Pilobolus* missile is one of the most fascinating objects in nature. A swollen cell beneath the black capsule that contains the spores is a genuinely light-sensitive "eye." This pigmented eye controls the direction of growth of the spore cannon and aims it very carefully at the region of greatest light in order that no intervening obstacle may block the flight of the spore capsule.

When a pressure of several atmospheres has been built up chemically within the cell underlying the spore container, the cell explodes, blasting the capsule several feet into the air. Since firing takes place in the morning hours, the stalks point to the sun at an angle sure to carry the tiny "rocket" several feet away as well as up. Tests in which the light has been reduced to a small spot indicate that the firing eye aims with remarkable accuracy. The spore vessel itself is so equipped with a quick-drying glue as to adhere to vegetation always in the proper position. Rain will not wash it off, and there it waits an opportunity to be taken up by munching cattle in order that *Pilobolus* can continue its travels through the digestive tract of the herbivores.

The tiny black capsule that bears the living spores through space is strangely reminiscent, in minature, of man's latest adventure. Man, too, is a spore bearer. The labor of millions and the consumption of vast stores of energy are necessary to hurl just a few individuals, perhaps eventually people of both sexes, on the road toward another planet. Similarly, for every spore city that arises in the fungus world, only a few survivors find their way into the future.

It is useless to talk of transporting the excess population of our planet elsewhere, even if a world of sparkling water and green trees were available. In nature it is a law that the spore cities die, but the spores fly on to find their destiny. Perhaps this will prove to be the rule of the newborn planet virus. Somehow in the *mysterium* behind genetics, the tiny pigmented eye and the rocket capsule were evolved together.

In an equal mystery that we only pretend to understand, man, in the words of Garet Garrett, "reached with his mind into emptiness and seized the machine." Deathly though some of its effects have proved, robber of the earth's crust though it may appear at this human stage to be, perhaps there are written within the machine two ultimate possibilities. The first, already, if primitively, demonstrated, is that of being a genuine spore bearer of the first complex organism to cross the barrier of the void. The second is that of providing the means by which man may someday be able to program his personality, or its better aspects, into the deathless machine itself, and thus escape, or nearly escape, the mortality of the body.

This may well prove to be an illusory experiment, but we who stand so close under the green primeval shade may still be as incapable of evaluating the human future as the first ape-man would have been to chart the course of *Homo sapiens*. There are over one hundred thousand spores packed in a single capsule of *Pilobolus,* and but few such capsules will ever reach their destiny. This is the way of the spore cities, in the infinite prodigality of nature. It may well be the dictum that controls the fate of man. Perhaps Rome drove blindly toward it and failed in the marches of the West. In the dreaming Buddhist cities that slowly ebbed away beneath the jungle, something was said that lingers, not entirely forgotten—namely, "Thou canst not travel on the Path before thou hast become the Path itself." Perhaps written deep in ourselves is a simulacrum of the Way and the mind's deep spaces to travel. If so, our goal is light-years distant, even though year by year the gantries lengthen over the giant rockets.

Man possesses the potential power to reach all the planets in this system. None, so far as can be presently determined, offers the prospects of extended colonization. The journey, however, will be undertaken as President Nixon has announced. It will be pursued because the technological and psychological commitment to space is too great for Western culture to abandon. In spite of the breadth of the universe we have previously surveyed, a nagging hope persists that someday, by means unavailable at present, we might achieve the creation of a rocket ship operating near the speed of light. At this point we would enter upon unknown territory, for it has been argued on the basis of relativity theory that men in such a mechanism might exist on a different time scale and age less rapidly than man upon earth. Assuming that such were the case, a question arises whether such a ship, coasting around the galaxy or beyond, might return to find life on our planet long departed. The disparities and the problems are great, and the conflicts of authorities have not made them less so.

It has been pointed out that so great a physicist as Sir Ernest Rutherford, as late as 1936, had pronounced the use of nuclear energy to be Utopian, at least within this century. Similar speculations on the part of others suggest that a great scientist's attempts to extrapolate his knowledge into the future may occasionally prove as inaccurate as the guesses of laymen. Scientific training is apt to produce a restraint, laudable enough in itself, that can readily degenerate into a kind of institutional conservatism. Darwin saw and commented upon this in his time. History has a way of outguessing all of us, but she does it in retrospect.

Nevertheless, because man is small and growing ever lonelier in his expanding universe, there remains a question he is unlikely ever to be able to answer. It involves the discovery of other civilizations in the cosmos. In some three billion years of life on this planet, man, who occupies a very small part of the geological time scale, is the one creature of earth who has achieved the ability to reason on a high abstract level. He has only grasped the nature of the stars within the last few generations. The number of such stars in the universe cannot be counted. Some may possess planets. Judging by our own solar system, of those planets few will possess life. Fewer still, infinitely fewer, will possess what could be called "civilizations" developed by other rational creatures.

On the basis of pure statistical chance, the likelihood that such civilizations are located in our portion of the galaxy is very small. Man's end may well come upon him long before he has had time to locate or even to establish the presence of other intelligent creatures in the universe. There are far more stars in the heavens than there are men upon the earth. The waste to be searched is too great for the powers we possess. In gambling terms, the percentage lies all with the house, or rather with the universe. Lonely though we may feel ourselves to be, we must steel ourselves to the fact that man, even far future man, may pass from the scene without possessing either negative or positive evidence of the existence of other civilized beings in this or other galaxies.

This is said with all due allowance for the fact that we may learn to make at least some satellites or planets within our own solar system artificially capable, in a small way, of sustaining life. For man to spread widely on the dubious and desert worlds of this sun system is unlikely. Much more unlikely is the chance that coursing at near the speed of light over a single arm of this galaxy would ever reveal intelligence, even if it were there. The speed would be too high and the planetary body too small. The size of our near neighbors, Mars and Venus, is proportionately tiny beside the sun's diameter or even that of the huge outer planets, Jupiter and Saturn.

I have suggested that man-machines and finally pure

intelligent machines— the product of a biology and a computerized machine technology beyond anything this century will possess—might be launched by man and dispersed as his final spore flight through the galaxies. Such machines would not need to trouble themselves with the time problem and, as the capsules of *Pilobolus* carry spores, might even be able to carry refrigerated human egg cells held in suspended animation and prepared to be activated, educated, and to grow up alone under the care of the machines.

The idea is fantastically wasteful, but so is life. It would be sufficient if the proper planetary conditions were discovered once in a thousand times. These human-machine combinations are much spoken of nowadays under the term "cyborg"—a shorthand term for "cybernetic organism." The machine structures would be intimately controlled by the human brain but built in such a manner as to amplify and extend the powers of the human personality. Other machines might be controlled by human beings deliberately modified by man's increasing knowledge of micro-surgery and genetics. Science has speculated that man has reached an evolutionary plateau. To advance beyond that plateau he must either intimately associate himself with machines in a new way or give way to "exosomatic evolution" and, in some fashion, transfer himself and his personality to the machine.

These are matters of the shadowy future and must be considered only as remote possibilities. More likely is the stricture that, even if we do not destroy ourselves as a planet virus, we will exhaust the primary resources of earth before we can produce the kind of spore carriers of which we dream. Again, the conception may lie forever beyond us. There is a certain grandeur, however, in the thought of man in some far future hour battling against oblivion by launching a final spore flight of cyborgs through the galaxy —a haven-seeking flight projected by those doomed never to know its success or failure, a flight such as life itself has always engaged in since it arose from the primeval waters.

One must repeat that nature is extravagant in the expenditure of individuals and germ cells. Our remote half-human ancestors gave themselves and never expected, or got, an answer as to the destiny their descendants might serve or if, indeed, they would survive. This is still the road we tread in the twentieth century. Sight of the future is denied us, and life was never given to be bearable. To what far creature, whether of metal or of flesh, we may be the bridge, no word informs us. If such a being is destined to come, there can be no assurance that it will spare a thought for the men who, in the human dawn, prepared its way. Man is a part of that torrential living river, which, since the beginning, has instinctively known the value of dispersion. He will yearn therefore to spread beyond the planet he now threatens to devour. This thought persists and is growing. It is rooted in the psychology of man.

A story has been told of the founder of one of the world's great religions—a religion which seeks constantly, in its higher manifestations, to wipe clean the mirror of the mind. Buddha is reported to have said to his sorrowing disciples as he lay dying, "Walk on." He wanted his people to be free of earthly entanglement or desire. That is how one should go in dignity to the true harvest of the worlds. It is a philosophy transferred from the old sun civilizations of earth. It implies that one cannot proceed upon the path of human transcendence until one has made interiorly in one's soul a road into the future. This is the warning of one who knew that the spaces within stretch as far as those without. Cyborgs and exosomatic evolution, however far they are carried, partake of the planet virus. They will never bring peace to man, but they will harry him onward through the circle of the worlds.

II

A scientific civilization in the full sense is an anomaly in world history. The civilizations of the sun never developed it. Only one culture, that of the West, has, through technology, reduced the religious mystique so long attatched to agriculture. Never before have such large masses of people been so totally divorced from the land or the direct processing of their own foodstuffs.

This phenomenon has undoubtedly contributed to the alienation of man from nature, as more and more acres go under cement for parking lots, shopping centers, and superhighways. A steadily mounting population threatens increasing damage to the natural environment from which food and breathable air are drawn. All kinds of sidelong, not very visible or dramatic dangers lurk about the edges of such an unstable situation. Any one of them could at some point become lethal, and an obscure and ignored problem turn into a disaster.

The tragedy of a single man in the New York blackout in 1965 could easily become the symbol for an entire civilization. This man, as it happened, was trapped by the darkness on an upper floor of a skyscraper. A Negrito or any one of the bush folk would have known better than to go prowling in a spirit-haunted, leopard-infested jungle after nightfall. The forest dwellers would have remained in their huts until daybreak.

In this case civilized man was troubled by no such inhibitions. Seizing a candle from a desk in his office, he made his way out into the corridor. Since the elevators were not running, he cast about for a stairway. Sighting what in the candlelight appeared to be a small service doorway near the bank of elevators, he opened it and, holding his small candle at eye level, stepped in. He was found the next day at the bottom of an elevator shaft, the extinguished candle still clutched in his hand.

I have said that this episode is symbolic. Man, frail, anticipatory man, no longer possessed the caution to find his way through a disturbance in his nightly routine. Instead he had seized a candle, the little flickering light of human knowledge, with which to confront one of his own giant creations in the dark. A janitor had left a door unlocked that should have been secured. Urban man, used to walking on smooth surfaces, had never glanced below his feet. He and his inadequate candle had plunged recklessly forward and been swallowed up as neatly by a machine in its tunnel as by a leopard on a dark path.

I have seen similar errors made at the onset of floods by men who no longer had the wit or conditioning to harken to the whispered warnings of wild nature. They had grown too confident of the powers of their own world, from which nature, so they thought, had been excluded. In the wider context of civilization, our candle flame may illuminate the next few moments but scarcely more. The old precarious world from which we came lurks always behind the door. It will find a way to be present, even if we should force it to retreat to the nearest star. Moreover, if, after the crust of the earth has been rifled and its resources consumed, civilization were to come upon evil times, man would have to start over with incredibly less than lay potentially before the flint users of the Ice Age.

But there emerges to haunt us the question of why this peculiar civilization arose. In the first part of the twentieth century appeared a man destined to be widely read, criticized, and contended against, even to be called wicked. He was destined to influence the philosophical historians who followed him in the attempt to observe some kind of discernible pattern in the events of history. Our concern with this man, Oswald Spengler, and his book, *The Decline of the West*, relates to just one aspect of Spengler's thought: the rise of our scientific civilization. That Spengler is periodically declared outmoded or resurrected need not involve us. What does affect us is that the man is basically a German poet-philosopher who glimpsed the leitmotif of the era we have been discussing and who pictured it well. It is the world in which we of the West find ourselves. Spengler is difficult, but in this aspect of his work he pictures the idea forms, the *zeitgeist*, lurking within the culture from which the rocket was to emerge.

Perhaps what he terms the Faustian culture—our own —began as early as the eleventh century with the growing addiction to great unfillable cathedrals with huge naves and misty recesses where space seemed to hover without limits. In the words of one architect, the Gothic arch is "a bow always tending to expand." Hidden within its tensions is the upward surge of the space rocket.

Again, infinite solitude tormented the individual soul. A too guilty hunger for forbidden knowledge beset the introverted heroes of this culture. The legend of Faust to this day epitomizes the West; the Quest of the Holy Grail is another of its Christian symbols. The bell towers of Western Europe have rung of time and death and burial in a way characteristic of no other culture. The bells were hung high and intended to reach far across space.

Faustian man is never at rest in the world. He is never the contemplative beneath the sacred Bô tree of the Buddha. He is, instead, a spokesman of the will. He is the embodiment of a restless, exploratory, and anticipating ego. In that last word we have the human head spun round to confront its future—the future it has created. It well may be that the new world, which began amidst time-tolling bells and the stained glass and dim interiors of Gothic cathedrals, laid an enchantment upon the people of Western Europe that provided at least a portion of the seedbed for the later rise of science—just as guilt has also haunted us. In its highest moments, science could also be said, not irreverently, to be a search for the Holy Grail. There the analogy lies—a poet's vision perhaps, but a powerful one. I would merely add one observation: that the owl, Minerva's symbol of wisdom, is able to turn its head through an angle of one hundred sixty degrees. It can be not visually anticipatory alone, it can look backward. Perhaps it is the lack of this ability that gives modern man and his children a slightly inhuman cast of countenance.

The Spore Bearers ✱ 85

III

Giordano Bruno was burned at Rome in 1600. His body perished, but the ideas for which he died—the heretical concepts of the great depths of the universe and of life on other worlds—ran on with similar dreams across the centuries to enlighten our own time. Space travel unconsciously began when the first hunters took their bearings on the North Star or saw the rising of the Southern Cross. It grew incipiently with the mathematics and the magnetic needle of the mariners. Man, in retrospect, seems almost predestined for space. To master the dream in its entirety, however, man had to invent in two categories: inventions of power and inventions of understanding. The invention of the scientific method itself began as an adventure in understanding. Inventions of power without understanding have been the bane of human history.

The word "invention" can denote ideas far removed from the machines to which the people of our mechanically inclined era seek constantly to limit the word. Let us take one refined example. The zero, invented twice in the mists of prehistory, once by the Hindus and once by the Maya, lies at the root of all complicated mathematics, yet it is not a "thing." Rather, it is a "no thing," a "nothing," without which Roman mathematics was a heavy, lumbering affair. In our time that necessary zero leaps instantaneously through the circuits of computers, helping to guide a rocket on the long pathway to Mars. One might say that an unknown mathematical genius seeking pure abstract understanding was a necessary prehistoric prelude to the success of the computer. He was also, and tragically, the possible indirect creator of world disaster in the shape of atomic war.

"Traveling long journeys is costly, at all times troublesome, at some times dangerous," warned a seventeenth-century writer. These were true words spoken of great seas and unmapped continents. They can also be spoken of the scientific journey itself. Today, magnified beyond the comprehension of that ancient wayfarer, we contemplate roads across the planetary orbits, the penetration of unknown atmospheres, and the defiance of solar flares. This effort has become the primary obsession of the great continental powers. Into the organization of this endeavor has gone an outpouring of wealth and inventive genius so vast that it constitutes a public sacrifice equivalent in terms of relative wealth to the building of the Great Pyramid at Giza almost five thousand years ago. Indeed, there is a sense in which modern science is involved in the construction of just such a pyramid, though an invisible one.

Science, too, demands great sacrifice, persistence of purpose across the generations, and an almost religious devotion. Whether its creations will loom to future ages as strangely antiquated as the sepulchres of the divine pharaohs, time alone will tell. Perhaps, in the final reckoning, only understanding will enable man to look back upon his pathway. For if inventions of power outrun understanding, as they now threaten to do, man may well sink into a night more abysmal than any he has yet experienced. Understanding increasingly begets power, but, as perceptive statesmen have long observed, power in the wrong hands has a way of corrupting understanding.

The Spore Bearers ✦ 87

There is an eye atop Palomar Mountain that peers at fleeing galaxies so remote that eons have elapsed since the light which reaches that great lens began its journey. There is another eye, that of the electron microscope, which peers deep into our own being. Both eyes are important. They are eyes of understanding. They balance and steady each other. They give our world perspective; they place man where he belongs. Such eyes, however, are subject to their human makers. Men may devise or acquire, and use beautiful or deathly machines and yet have no true time sense, no tolerance, no genuine awareness of their own history. By contrast, the balanced eye, the rare true eye of understanding, can explore the gulfs of history in a night or sense with uncanny accuracy the subtle moment when a civilization in all its panoply of power turns deathward. There are such troubled seers among us today —men who fear that the ramifications of the huge industrial complex centering upon space is draining us of energy and wealth for other enterprises—that it has about it a threatening, insensitive, and cataclysmic quality.

A term in military parlance, "the objective," may be pertinent here. It is intended to secure the mind against the diffuse and sometimes inept opportunism of the politician, or the waves of uninformed emotion to which the general public is so frequently subjected. An objective is delimited with precision and care. Its intention is to set a clearly defined goal. Armies, or for that matter sciences, do not advance on tides of words. Instead, they must be supplied logistically. Schedules must equate with a realistic appraisal of resources.

There will never be enough men or material for a multitudinous advance on all fronts—even for a wealthy nation. Thus, as our technological feats grow more costly, the objectives of our society must be assessed with care. From conservation to hospitals, from defense to space, we are forced by circumstance to live more constantly in the future. Random "tinkering," random response to the unexpected, become extraordinarily costly in the industrial world which Western society has created. Yet, paradoxically, the unexpected comes with increasing rapidity upon future-oriented societies such as ours. Psychological stresses appear. The current generation feels increasingly alienated from its predecessors. There is a quickening of vibrations running throughout the society. One might, in physiological terms, say that its metabolism has been feverishly accelerated. For this, a certain price in stability has been exacted, the effects of which may not be apparent until long afterward.

The attempt to conquer space has seized the public imagination. To many of this generation, the sight of rockets roaring upward has brought home the feats of science so spectacularly that we sometimes forget the medical researcher brooding in his laboratory, or the archaeologist striving amidst broken shards and undeciphered hieroglyphs to understand what doom destroyed a city lying beneath the sands of centuries. The estimated cost of placing the unmanned Surveyor 3 upon the moon amounted to more than eighty million dollars. Just one unmanned space probe, in other words, equaled or exceeded the entire endowment of many a good college or university; the manned flight of Apollo 12 cost two hundred and fifty millions. The total space program is inconceivably costly, yet the taxpayer, up until recently, accepted it with little question. By contrast, his elected officials frequently boggle over the trifling sums necessary to save a redwood forest or to clear a river of pollution.

What then, we are forced to ask, is our objective? Is it scientific? Is it purely military? Or is it these and more? Is there some unconscious symbolism at work? At heart, does each one of us, when a rocket hurtles into space, yearn once more for some lost green continent under other skies? Is humanity, like some ripening giant puffball, feeling the mounting pressure of the spores within? Are we, remote though we may be from habitable planets, driven by the same irresistible migrating impulse that descends upon an overpopulated hive? Are we each unconsciously escaping from the mechanized routine and urban troubles which increasingly surround us? Beneath our conscious rationalizations does this play a role in our willingness to sustain the growing burden?

Any answers to these questions would be complex and would vary from individual to individual. They are worth asking because they are part of the venture in understanding that is necessary to human survival. Two successful moon landings, it goes without saying, are an enormous intellectual achievement. But what we must try to understand is more difficult than the mathematics of a moon shot —namely, the nature of the scientific civilization we are in the process of creating. Science has risen in a very brief interval into a giant social institution of enormous prestige and governmentally suported power. To many, it replaces primitive magic as the solution for all human problems.

IV

In the coastal jungles of eastern Mexico the archaeologist comes at intervals upon giant stone heads of many tons weight carved in a strikingly distinct style far different from that of the Maya. They mark the remains of the lost Olmec culture of the first millennium before the Christian era. Around the globe, more that one such society of clever artisans has arisen and placed its stamp, the order of its style, upon surrounding objects, only to lapse again into the night of time. Each was self-contained. Each, with the limited amount of wealth and energy at its disposal, placed its greatest emphasis upon some human dream, some lost philosophy, some inner drive beyond the satisfaction of the needs of the body. Each, in turn, vanished.

Western man, with the triumph of the experimental method, has turned upon the world about him an intellectual instrument of enormous power never fully exploited by any previous society. Its feats of understanding include the discovery of evolutionary change as revealed in the stratified rocks. It has looked far down the scale of life to reveal man magically shrunken to a tiny tree shrew on a forest branch. Science has solved the mysteries of microbial disease and through the spectroscope has determined the chemical composition of distant stars. It has groped its way into a knowledge of the gigantic distances of the cosmos—distances too remote for short-lived man ever to penetrate. It has learned why the sun endures and at what pace light leaps across the universe.

Man can speak into infinite spaces, but in this time in which I write violence and contention rage, not alone on opposite sides of the world, but here at home. How far are all these voices traveling, I wonder? Out beyond earth's farthest shadow, on and on into the depths of the universe? And suppose that there were, out yonder, some hidden listening ear, would it be able to discern any difference between the sounds man made when he was a chittering tree shrew contesting for a beetle and those produced at his appearance before a parliament of nations?

It is a thing to consider, because with understanding arise instruments of power, which always spread faster than the inventions of calm understanding. The tools of violence appeal to the fanatic, the illiterate, the blindly venomous. The inventions of power have grown monstrous in our time. Man's newfound ingenuity has given him health, wealth, and increase, but there is added now the ingredient of an ever-growing terror. Man is only beginning dimly to discern that the ultimate menace, the final interior zero, may lie in his own nature. It is said in an old tale that to understand life man must learn to shudder. This century seems doomed to master the lesson.

Science, in spite of its awe-inspiring magnitude, contains one flaw that partakes of the nature of the universe itself. It can solve problems, but it also creates them in a genuinely confusing ratio. They escape unseen out of the laboratory into the body politic, whether they be germs inured to antibiotics, the waiting death in rocket silos, or the unloosed multiplying power of life. There are just so many masterful and inventive brains in the human population. Even with the growth of teamwork and the attempted solution of future problems now coming to be known as systems analysis, man is our most recalcitrant material. He does not yield cherished beliefs with rapidity;

he will not take pills at the decree of some distant, well-intentioned savior.

No one knows surely what was the purpose of Olmec art. We do know something of the seemingly endless political expansion and ethnic dilution that precipitated the fall of Rome. We know also that the pace of technological innovation in the modern world has multiplied throughout our lifetimes. The skills expended now upon space may in the end alter our philosophies and rewrite our dreams, even our very concepts of the nature of life—if there is life —beyond us in the void. Moreover the whole invisible pyramid is itself the incidental product of a primitive seed capsule, the human brain, whose motivations alter with time and circumstance.

In summary, we come round again to the human objective. In the first four million years of man's existence, or, even more pointedly, in the scant second's tick during which he has inhabited cities and devoted himself to an advanced technology, is it not premature to pronounce either upon his intentions or his destiny? Perhaps it is— as the first man-ape could not have foreseen the book-lined room in which I write. Yet something of that creature remains in me as he does in all men. I compose, or I make clever objects with what were originally a tree dweller's hands. Fragments of his fears, his angers, his desires, still stream like midnight shadows through the circuits of my brain. His unthinking jungle violence, inconceivably magnified, may determine our ending. Still, by contrast, the indefinable potentialities of a heavy-browed creature capable of pouring his scant wealth into the grave in a gesture of grief and self-abnegation may lead us at last to some triumph beyond the realm of technics. Who is to say?

The Spore Bearers ✳ 93

Not long ago, seated upon a trembling ladder leading to a cliff-house ruin that has not heard the voice of man for centuries, I watched, in a puff of wind, a little swirl of silvery thistledown rise out of the canyon gorge beneath my feet. One or two seeds fell among stony crevices about me, but another, rising higher and higher upon the light air, ascended into the blinding sunshine beyond my vision. It is like man, I thought briefly, as I resumed my climb. It is like man, inside or out, off to new worlds where the chances, the stairways, are infinite. But like the seed, he has to grow. That impulse, too, we bring with us from the ancestral dark.

Another explosion of shimmering gossamer circled about my head. I held to the rickety ladder and followed the erratic, windborne flight of seeds until it mounted beyond the constricting canyon walls and vanished. Perhaps the eruption of our giant rockets into space had no more significance than this, I saw finally, as in a long geological perspective. It was only life engaged once more on an old journey. Here, perhaps, was our supreme objective, hidden by secretive nature even from ourselves.

Almost four centuries ago, Francis Bacon, in the years of the voyagers, had spoken of the new world of science as "something touching upon hope." In such hope do all launched seeds participate. And so did I, did unstable man upon his ladder or his star. It was no more than that. Within, without, the climb was many-dimensioned and over imponderable abysses. I placed my foot more carefully and edged one step farther up the face of the cliff.

FIVE ❖ THE TIME EFFACERS

The savage mind deepens its knowledge with the help of imagines mundi.

—CLAUDE LÉVI-STRAUSS

THE TIME EFFACERS

There are two diametrically opposed forces forever at war in the heart of man: one is memory; the other is forgetfulness. No one knows completely the nature of the inner turmoil which creates this struggle. Some rare individuals possess almost total recall; others find certain events in life so painful that they are made to sink beneath the surface of consciousness. Sigmund Freud himself learned, as he practiced the arts of healing, to dip his hands into the dark waters which contain our lurking but suppressed memories. There are those among us who wish, even in death, not a name or a memory to survive.

Once I sat in the office of a county coroner, having come there at his request. We had previously had many discussions involving cases of human identification that had come his way. Some of his problems demanded the specialties of my own field, and though I am not an expert in forensic medicine I had been glad to listen to his experiences, as well as occasionally to offer advice on some anatomical point.

When I was ushered into his office on that particular afternoon, a carefully prepared skull gleamed upon his desk. My friend looked up at me with a grin of satisfaction. "You have told me something about what the archaeologist is able to infer concerning the habits of our remote ancestors," he said. "Now I would like you to look at this specimen. The body from which it came was discovered by accident in a drained pond. It had been there for some time and was almost totally decomposed."

I picked up the skull and slowly turned it over. A glitter of platinum wire immediately caught my eye. I drew the mandible aside. "Look," I said in surprise, "this is one of the most expensive and elaborate pieces of dental work I have ever seen."

"Precisely," said my friend. "The job was obviously done by a gifted specialist, and it could easily have cost a thousand dollars. So we know what?"

"That the individual had means and took care of himself," I sparred. "Surely an identification can be made on this basis."

Slowly the coroner shook his head. "We have tried," he said, "tried hard. The man did not come from around here. He came most probably from a far-off big city. It is in such places that this kind of work is done, but which place?"— he shrugged—"one could spend years on such a task and come up with nothing. Our office has neither the time, the staff, nor the money for such investigations, particularly if no evidence of a crime exists."

"You mean—?" I asked.

"Yes," he said, "it was very likely suicide by drowning."

"Then shouldn't there be some identification remaining —a wallet, a ring, something?"

My friend eyed me quizzically. "I wanted you to see this," he said, "not because skulls are new to you, but because you have always worked in the past—with another set of problems. What you see here in this individual specimen we encounter as a single category." He tapped the magnificent bridgework with a pencil to emphasize his point. "We find a certain persistent number of suicides—people like this one, very likely a man of wealth—who, when they have decided to depart this life, do so with the determination at the same time to obliterate their identity.

"Sometimes they travel far before the final act is carried out. At the last, every conceivable trace of identity is abandoned. Wallets with their cards may be hurled away, jewelry similarly disposed of; it is as though the individual were not satisfied to destroy himself, he must, as this man apparently did, bury his name so thoroughly that no one will be heard to pronounce it again."

"But murder," I interjected.

"Of course, of course, we have such cases and such concealment." He turned once more to the skull. "I tell you now, however, that their number is minute compared to these." He elevated the face and looked into it as if for an answer, but the skull stared beyond him unheeding and stubbornly triumphant.

The coroner sighed once more and eased the skull back upon the desk, a certain gentleness evident in his manner. "Well," he said, "I rather think this one will have his wish to be forgotten." He fingered one of the fine wires of the bridgework. "Strange," he added. "He took care of himself—up to the last, that is. You can see it here. But then this thing—this shadow, whatever it was—came on him until he was forced to flee out of the body itself. But no one, if there was by then anyone, was to witness his final defeat. He saw to it well; he had given it thought, he left us a blank wall. Except for a new drainage ditch we would not have found even this."

My friend gestured politely. "A kind of gentleman's end, don't you think?" he said. "Perhaps there was an intent to spare someone, somewhere; who knows? It would appear he came a long way for this and went to some trouble. I won't bother you with any more details. I just wanted you to know what can lurk in these little boxes you and your colleagues handle with such scientific precision. Here in this office we are forced to build a different world with the same bones." He gently touched the skull again. "They are individuals to me, not phenotypes."

"You mistake us," I countered, "if you think we are not aware of the darkness in the human mind. Have you never heard of the *damnatio memoriae*?"

The coroner's eyes twinkled.

"Of couse not," he said. "That is what I got you in here for, to stir me up." He leaned back expectantly.

"It is a different matter from the case of your anonymous client here," I explained slowly, "and is frequently done for obscure or depraved reasons. Do you know that history is full of evidence of hatred for the past, of a desire on the part of some men to destroy even the memory of their predecessors? Public monuments are effaced, names destroyed, histories rewritten. Sometimes to achieve these ends a whole intellectual elite may be massacred in order that the peasantry can be deliberately caused to forget its past. The erasure of history plays a formidable role in human experience. It extends from the smashing of the first commemorative monuments right down to the creation of the communist "non-person" of today. Carthage was a victim of that animus. So was the pharaoh Akhenaton, who introduced solar monotheism into Egypt."

I paused, but my friend the coroner only nodded. "Go on," he said.

"The French revolutionists sought from 1792 to 1805 permanently to eliminate the Christian calendar. Today's youth revolt is partly aimed at the destruction of the past and the humiliation of the previous generation. Just as the individual mind thrusts unwelcome thoughts below the level of consciousness, so there are times, when, in revulsion against painful or uncontainable thoughts and symbols, the social memory similarly reacts against itself. Or, again, it may reclothe old myths and traditions in new and more pleasing garments."

I pointed at the skull upon which my friend's hand rested. "Men get tired, you see. This man in the end wanted complete oblivion—not alone for his physical body —he wished to make sure he lived in no man's mind.

"The masses," I continued, "can be stirred by the same impulse. There are times of social disruption when they grow tired of history. If they cannot remake the past they intend at least to destroy it—efface the dark memory from their minds and so, in a sense, pretend that history has never been. There are plenty of examples—the assault of Cromwell's Puritans upon the statuary in the English cathedrals, or earlier, in Henry the Eighth's time, the breaking up of the great abbeys and the reckless dispersal of their ancient documents and treasures. Even worse was the total overthrow of Inca and Aztec civilization at the hands of the Spaniards. An entire writing system perished on the verge of the modern era."

The coroner's office seemed to grow darker from an

impending storm gathering outside. For a moment I had a feeling of inexplicable terror, as though both of us crouched in some cranny beside a torrent that was sweeping everything to destruction.

"What you are saying"—the coroner's voice came from somewhere beyond the skull—"is that to know time is to fear it, and to know civilized time is to be terror-stricken."

I nodded. The room grew oppressively dark. I felt an impulse, somewhat against my better judgment, to speak further. The skull had taken on a faintly watchful expression, as though it had in reality projected my thought. Beyond it, all seemed slipping into shadows.

"I am speaking as a gravedigger only," I said, my eyes fixed blindly forward. "But there is a paradox to all digging that only an archaeologist would understand. The best way to be resurrected is to be forgotten. Consider the case of Tutankhamen."

The coroner opened his window. The rain had begun to fall and its scent stole into the room along with a fresh breath of air.

"I know what you mean," he said, as the skull with its gleaming denture was deposited in a drawer. "Sometimes an individual, perhaps a great artist, or a civilization, has to be held off stage for a millennium or so until they can be understood. Like the art of Lascaux, fifteen thousand years forgotten in a sealed cave. In a case like that, even time has to be rediscovered. Not even discovered, but interpreted. It consists of more than the marks on a dial."

I arose and stood beside my friend, looking down on the wet pavement beneath us, where the rain was pushing fallen leaves along the gutter.

"Look," he said, waving a hand toward the street, "every culture in the world has a built-in clock, but in what other culture than ours has time been discovered to contain novelty? In what other culture would leaves, these yellow falling leaves, be said to be emergent and not eternal?"

"Evolutionary time," I added, "the time of the world-eaters—ourselves."

We both stood silent, watching below the window the serrated shapes of the leaves as they spun past in the gathering dark.

II

"Every man," Thoreau once recorded in his journal, "tracks himself through life." Thoreau meant that the individual in all his reading, his traveling, his observations, would follow only his own footprints through the snows of this world. He would see what his temperament dictated, hear what voices his ears allowed him to hear, and not one whit more. This is the fate of every man. What is less well known is that civilizations, which are the products of men, are in their way equally obtuse. They follow their own tracks through a time measurable in centuries or millennia, but they approach the final twilight with much the same set of postulates with which they began. In Ruth Benedict's words, they resemble a human personality thrown large upon the screen, given gigantic features and a long time span.

Of these personalities the most intensely aggressive has been that of the West, particularly in the last three centuries which have seen the rise of modern science. When I say "aggressive," I mean an increasingly time-conscious, future-oriented society of great technical skill, which has fallen out of balance with the natural world about it. First of all, it is a consumer society which draws into itself raw materials from remote regions of the globe. These it processes into a wide variety of goods which a high standard of living enables it to consume. This vast industrial activity, in turn, enables the scientist and technologist to take command of business.

Scientists are not necessarily rich or the owners of business. The process is more subtle. With the passage of time and the growth of the urban structure, funds for research and development take up a far greater proportion of the budget of a particular industry. So long as the industry is in competition with others, it cannot afford to cling for long to a particular industrial process because of the fear that rival technicians will develop something more attractive or cheaper. The drive for miniaturization in the computer industry is a case in point. Thus the laboratory and its priesthood take an increasing share of the profits as they become a necessity for business survival. They also intensify the rate of social change which contributes both to human expectations and the alienation between the generations. Advertising becomes similarly important in order to encourage the acceptance of the new products as they are made available to the public. National defense is swept into the same expensive pattern in the technological war for survival.

In simple terms, the rise of a scientific society means a society of constant expectations directed toward the oncoming future. What we have is always second best, what we expect to have is "progress." What we seek, in the end, is Utopia. In the endless pursuit of the future we have ended by engaging to destroy the present. We are the greatest producers of non-degradable garbage on the planet. In the cities a winter snowfall quickly turns black from the pollutants we have loosed in the atmosphere.

This is not to denigrate the many achievements and benefits of modern science. On a huge industrial scale, however, we have unconsciously introduced a mechanism which threatens to run out of control. We are tracking ourselves into the future—a future whose "progress" is as dubious as that which we experience today. Once the juggernaut is set in motion, to slow it down or divert its course is extremely difficult because it involves the livelihood and social prestige of millions of workers. The future becomes a shibboleth which chokes our lungs, threatens our ears with sonic booms, and sets up a population mobility which is destructive in its impact on social institutions.

In the extravagant pursuit of a future projected by science, we have left the present to shift for itself. We have regarded science as a kind of twentieth-century substitute for magic, instead of as a new and burgeoning social institution whose ways are just as worthy of objective study as our political or economic structures. In short, the future has become our primary obsession. We constantly treat our scientists as soothsayers and project upon them questions involving the destiny of man over prospective millions of years.

As evidence of our insecurity, these questions multiply with our technology. We are titillated and reassured by articles in the popular press sketching the ways in which the new biology will promote our health and longevity, while, at the other end of the spectrum, hovers the growing shadow of a locust swarm of human beings engendered by our successful elimination of famine and plague. To meet this threat to our standard of living we are immediately encouraged to believe in a "green revolution" brought about by ingenious plant scientists. That the green revolution, even if highly successful, would not long restore the balance between nature and man, goes unremarked.

Thus science, as it leads men further and further from the first world they inhabited, the world we call natural, into a new and unguessed domain, is beguiling them. In a world where contingencies multiply at a fantastic rate and nations react like fevered patients whose metabolism is seriously disturbed, the scientist is forced into a new and hitherto unsought role in society. From the seclusion of the laboratory he is being drawn into the role of an Eastern seer, with all the dangers and exacerbations this entails. To shepherd the recalcitrant masses, or indeed to guide himself safely through a world of his own unconscious creation, is a well-nigh impossible task which has come upon him by insidious degrees. He does not possess marked political power, yet he has transformed the world in which power operates.

The scientist is now in the process of learning that the social world is stubbornly indifferent to the elegant solutions of the lecture hall, and that to guide a future-oriented world along the winding path to Utopia demands an omniscience that no human being possesses. We have long passed the simple point at which science presented to us beneficent medicines and where, in the words of José Ortega y Gasset, science and the civilization shaped by it could be regarded as the self-objectivation of human reason. It is one thing successfully to plan a moon voyage; it is quite another to solve the moral problems of a distraught, unenlightened, and confused humanity.

Men wandering in the infinitude of space and time which their science has revealed are trapped in a world of darkening shadows, like those depicted in Giambattista Piranesi's eighteenth-century etchings, the *Carceri.* The pictures reveal giant buildings in which the human figure wanders lost amidst huge beams and winding stairways ascending or descending into vacancy. Thick ropes hang from spiked machines of unspeakable intent. This world of the prisons is the world of man; the vast maze offers no exit.

Unlike the cyclic time of the classical world, the time of the Christian era is novel. It proceeds to an end and it has arisen through a creative act. Though science has enormously extended the cosmic calendar, it has never succeeded in eliminating that foreknowledge of the non-existence of life and of individual genera and species which the Christian creation introduced. We bear in our actual bodies traces of our formation out of the animal remnants of the past. Thus causality plays a significant role in our thinking because we have been stitched together from the bones and tissues of creatures which are now extinct.

As our knowledge of the evolutionary past has increased, we have unconsciously transferred the observed complexity of forms leading up through the geological strata to our cultural behavior. We speak of "progress" in a rather ill-defined way, and from surveying time past we have become devotees of time future. We maintain "think tanks" in which experts are employed to play all possible games, to create models, military or otherwise, that the future might produce. We are handicapped in just one way: the future may be guessed at, but only as a series of unknown alternatives.

Some decades ago Henry Phillips of the Massachusetts Institute of Technology expressed this dilemma succinctly. "What will happen five minutes from now is pretty well determined," he wrote, "but as that period is gradually lengthened a larger and larger number of purely accidental occurrences are included. Ultimately a point is reached beyond which events are more than half determined by accidents which have not yet happened. Present planning loses significance when that point is reached. . . . Here is the fundamental dilemma of civilization . . . there is serious doubt whether the way forward is known."

Mathematical statistics arose as a technique for achieving some insight into the contingencies of life—that is, variable phenomena. This technique does not, however, aid us in discerning those events which Dr. Phillips describes as not yet having happened. It can, at best, inform us that the urban mass is reaching fantastic numbers and that the birthrate must be reduced. Of the end result of these phenomena, as of pollution, it can tell us little. It can only inform us that the trends which are extrapolated into the future spell disaster. Infinitesimal man is beginning to draw the macrocosm into himself, or, rather, it might be stated that through his evolutionary advancement the cosmos is beginning to reach into him. He has yet to prove that he can master the powers he has summoned up.

Man, oriented completely toward the future, suppresses

his past as dissatisfying. He unconsciously resents continuity and causality; he is *event*-oriented. This is frequently reflected in the new motion pictures made to appeal to a youthful audience. Plot gives way to episode. The existential world of the hippy provokes sensate experience but does not demand dramatic continuity. The result is the onset of that chaos in which societal order threatens to disappear.

Thus, with the near destruction of emotional continuity between the generations, time past is vilified or extinguished in favor of oncoming uncoordinated activist time. "Make the revolution," exhorts one youngster. "Afterwards we will decide what to to do about it." Another pauses merely to exclaim, "Scrap the system." With those words, we have reached the final culmination of the Faustian hunger for experience. Creative time has been obliterated in order to welcome something new in human history—the pure and disconnected "event" that has replaced reality. The LSD trip has reached a level with the experience of the classroom. It is not a coincidence that the memory effacers have emerged in the swarming time of the spore cities. Man has followed his own tracks in a circle as great as that of the cometary visitant from space that had ushered in my childhood.

III

As an anthropologist I once came upon time wrapped in a small leathern bag—a bag such as that in which Odysseus might once have carried the four winds. The way of the matter was this. It was a small Pawnee medicine bundle. The bundle, among other objects, contained some feathers, a mineralized fossil tooth, an archaic, square-headed iron nail, and a beautifully flaked Ice Age spearpoint of agate. The date of the latter was easy to identify because of its shape, which related it immediately to a long-gone mammoth-hunting people.

The warrior to whom this precious bundle had once belonged must have had an alert eye for the things his guardian spirit had advised him to seek. There was no way of telling from this cracked receptacle what powers had been given its possessor or what had been his dreams. They had come swirling, presumably upon demand, from that dark region which contains the past. The square-headed nail represented the man's own time, but it had obviously been regarded as too sacred to hammer into an arrowpoint.

Most probably all this contained past in the little bundle was filled with streaming darkness and sudden emergences. For, as Joseph Campbell has so aptly pointed out, "where there is magic there is no death." I was not so insensitive in undoing the crumbling hide that I failed to feel the shadow of an extinct animal, or touch with longing the intricately flaked weapon of a vanished day. The bundle held in my hand had been a sacred object among a people who believed implicitly in its powers and who understood the prayers and fastings through which the owner had been instructed. I was an outsider to whom the nail could never denote more than a nail, or the flaked weapon stand for more than a bygone historical moment. I was afflicted by causality, by technological time rather than the magic of genuine earth time.

I have spoken of the time effacers in Western culture as those who would destroy all memory of the dead or, turning from the ancient institutions which have sustained our society, would engage in an orgiastic and undiscriminating embrace of the episodic moment—the statistical happening without significance. The deliberate effacement of defeated men and broken cultures is, as I have said, an ancient act in world history. The attempt to leap forward into the future or grudgingly to accept the fleeting moment as the only abode of man is particularly a phenomenon of our turbulent era. The causes I have to some degree explored. I have not, however, paused to examine the nature of time in those simple cultures which are without causal or novel time, and where the veil between life and death wavers fitfully at best. Borders are undefined, and animals or men, rather easily exchanging shapes, pass to and fro in ways unknown to the sophisticated world.

Certainly this world of the primitive is a novel one by civilized standards, but not in terms of primitive thought. There are several reasons why this is so. The distinctions between animals and men that have been established by biological science do not obtain in the primitive mind. Animals talk, they carry messages, they may be supernaturals. Time itself may exhibit highly eccentric behavior. It may stand still, as it does to those who intrude into fairyland, or again, two kinds of time, the time of human beings and the time of the supernaturals, may exist side by side. This last is a phenomenon on which it would be advisable to dwell for a moment. It is highly characteristic of many peoples outside the urban swarming phase. It tells us something of the psychology of man while he still clung to the savage environment from which he had arisen.

With the Australian aborigines, for example, there are two separate time scales: that of the immediate present, the common day of ordinary existence, and, in addition, that of the period of "dreamtime" or dawn beings which precedes the workaday world. This latter epoch is a sacred, mythological era in which man was first created and in which the supernatural beings laid down the laws that have since governed him.

The past of the dreamtime, however, is not really past at all. The world, it is true, perhaps no longer visibly responds to the forces that were exerted in the time the ancestors. Nevertheless the atmosphere of the dreamtime still persists, like an autumnal light, across the landscape of the aborigines. It is elusive, it is immaterial, but it is there. The divine beings still exist, even though they may have shifted form or altered their abodes. Man survives by their aid and sufferance. He did not come into existence merely once at their behest. They are still his preceptors and guides. They continue to order his ways in the difficult environment that surrounds him—a countryside that has been appropriately described as his living age-old family tree.

Totemic rituals establish for each generation the living reality of man's relationship to the plant and animal world which sustains him. His occupations came from the totemic ancestors. Thus man, in his human time, subsists also in a kind of surviving dreamtime which is eternal and unchanging. Both men and animals come and go through the generations a little like actors slipping behind the curtain, in order to reappear later, drawn through the totemic center to precisely similar renewed roles in society. Sacred time is of another and higher dimension than secular time.

It is, in reality, timeless; past and future are contained within it. All of primitive man's meaningful relationship to his world is thus not history, not causality in a scientific sense, but a mythical ordering of life which has not deviated and will not in future deviate from the traditions of eternity.

The emergence of novel events has no meaning to the timeless people. Sacred time enables man to escape from or, to a degree, to ignore the profane time in which he actually exists. Among the world's most simple people, we find remarkably effective efforts to erase or ignore all that is not involved with the transcendent search for timelessness, the happy land of no change. Perhaps this was what Plato sought in his doctrine of the forms—the world beyond reality so poetically expressed by Margaret Mead as the "world of the first rose, and the first lark song."

Perhaps at this stage of human culture man has sought psychic protection for himself by buttressing the stability of his environment. In his own fashion, he has remolded nature in mytho-poetic terms. He lives his life amidst talking animals and the marks of the going and coming of the dream divinities who are both his creators and the guardians of his days. As closely as a mortal can manage, he exists in eternity.

In this stage, in spite of numerous variations in religious practice over the world, man is basically not a consciously malicious time effacer. He is, instead, a creature to whom secular time has no meaning and no value; he is living in the perpetual light of a past dreamtime which still enfolds him. He is at peace with the seasons and, through decreed ritual, even with the animals he hunts. Frequently he is terrified by the unusual when it is thrust too prominently before his eyes or cannot be fitted into his accepted cosmology.

This world, a world that man has inhabited for a far longer period than high civilization has existed upon earth, contrasts spectacularly with the secular domain of science. If it is illusory, we must admit that it is at the same time relatively stable. Man lived safely within the confines of nature. A few stones from the riverbed, a bit of shaped clay, some wild seeds, and a receptacle made of bark perhaps sufficed him. On a subsistence level of economic activity, the primitives had actually arrived at an ecological balance with nature. They had created another world of reentry into that nature upon a psychical level. One might say that, like a turtle, man had thrust out his curious head just far enough to glimpse the harshness of the profane landscape and had quickly chosen to mythologize and thereby make peace with it. On a simple basis he had achieved what modern man in his thickening shell of technology is only now seeking unsuccessfully to accomplish.

Man, in other words, is not by innate psychology a world eater. He possesses, in his far-ranging mind, only the latent potentiality. The rise of Western urbanism, accompanied by science, produced the world eaters just as surely as those other less sophisticated primitives reentered nature by means of the sacred, never-to-be-disturbed time that was not, except as it developed in their heads.

So vast is the gap that now yawns between the degraded remnants of the hunting folk and their brothers, the world eaters, that even a perceptive anthropologist of a generation ago, Paul Radin, was not prepared in the atmosphere of his time to recognize the unconscious irony in the conclusion of his book *The World of Primitive Man*. After narrating many things about the Eskimo and their philosophy, including their abhorrence of overweening pride, Radin quotes the statement of one Eskimo who had been taken to New York. After gazing down into the great canyons of the streets, the wondering native finally remarked, according to Radin's informant, "Nature is great but man is greater still." One can understand the confusion of an Eskimo brought from far ice fields to peer down upon the greatest city of the world eaters. More appalling is the discovery that an anthropologist could have quoted this simple remark with approbation as a profound message to modern man. The irony is deepened when we learn that nature sends no messages to man when all is well.

If the message which Radin interpreted was sent, perhaps, like so many messages from the dark powers, it should have been read with a different emphasis. When man becomes greater than nature, nature, which gave him birth, will respond. She has dealt with the locust swarm and she has led the lemmings down to the sea. Even the world eaters will not be beyond her capacities. Sila, as the Eskimo call nature, remains apart from mankind *just as long as men do not abuse life*." This is the message that a more able shaman might have found a raven to carry—a raven who could still wing with an undefaced warning from the country of primeval time.

SIX ✣ MAN IN
THE AUTUMN LIGHT

There will always be those who must look into the dark in order to see.

—ALAN MC GLASHAN

MAN IN
THE AUTUMN LIGHT

The French dramatist Jean Cocteau has argued persuasively about the magic light of the theatre. People must remember, he contended, that "the theatre is a trick factory where truth has no currency, where anything natural has no value, where the only things that convince us are card tricks and sleights of hand of a difficulty unsuspected by the audience."

The cosmos itself gives evidence, on an infinitely greater scale, of being just such a trick factory, a set of lights forever changing, and the actors themselves shape shifters, elongated shadows of something above or without. Perhaps in the sense men use the word natural, there is really nothing at all natural in the universe or, at best, that the world is natural only in being unnatural, like some variegated, color-shifting chameleon.

In Brazilian rivers there exists a fish, one of the cyprinodonts, which sees with a two-lensed eye, a kind of bifocal adjustment that permits the creature to examine the upper world of sunlight and air, while with the lower half of the lens he can survey the watery depths in which he lives. In this quality the fish resembles Blake, the English poet who asserted he saw with a double vision into a farther world than the natural. Now the fish, we might say, looks simultaneously into two worlds of reality, though what he makes of this divided knowledge we do not know. In the case of man, although there are degrees of seeing, we can observe that the individual has always possessed the ability to escape beyond naked reality into some other dimension, some place outside the realm of what might be called "facts."

Man is no more natural than the world. In reality he is, as we have seen, the creator of a phantom universe, the universe we call culture—a formidable realm of cloud shapes, ideas, potentialities, gods, and cities, which with man's death will collapse into dust and vanish back into "expected" nature.

Some landscapes, one learns, refuse history; some efface it so completely it is never found; in others the thronging memories of the past subdue the living. In my time I have experienced all these regions, but only in one place has the looming future overwhelmed my sense of the present. This happened in a man-made crater on the planet earth, but to reach that point it is necessary to take the long way round and to begin where time had lost its meaning. As near as I can pinpoint the place, it was somewhere at the edge of the Absaroka range along the headwaters of the Bighorn years ago in Wyoming. I had come down across a fierce land of crags and upland short-grass meadows, past aspens shivering in the mountain autumn. It was the season of the golden light. I was younger then and a hardened foot traveler. But youth had little to do with what I felt. In that country time did not exist. There was only the sound of water hurrying over pebbles to an unknown destination

—water that made a tumult drowning the sound of human voices.

Somewhere along a creek bank I stumbled on an old archaeological site whose beautifully flaked spearpoints of jasper represented a time level remote from me by something like ten thousand years. Yet, I repeat, this was a country in which time had no power because the sky did not know it, the aspens had not heard it passing, the river had been talking to itself since before man arose, and in that country it would talk on after man had departed.

I was alone with the silvery aspens in the mountain light, looking upon time thousands of years remote, yet so meaningless that at any moment flame might spurt from the ash of a dead campfire and the hunters come slipping through the trees. My own race had no role in these mountains and would never have.

I felt the light again, the light that was falling across the void on other worlds. No bird sang, no beast stirred. To the west the high ranges with their snows rose pure and cold. It was a place to meet the future quite as readily as the past. The fluttering aspens expressed no choice, and I, a youngster with but few memories, chose to leave them there. The place was of no true season, any more than the indifferent torrent that poured among the boulders through summer and deep snow alike.

I camped in a little grove as though waiting, filled with a sense of incompleteness, alert for some intangible message that was never uttered. The philosopher Jacques Maritain once remarked that there is no future thing for God. I had come upon what seemed to be a hidden fragment of the days before creation. Because I was mortal and not an omniscient creature, I lingered beside the stream

Man in the Autumn Light ✦ 121

with a growing restlessness. I had brought time in my perishable body into a place where, to all intents, it could not exist. I was moving in a realm outside of time and yet dragging time with me in an increasingly excruciating effort. If man was a creature obliged to choose, then choice was here denied me. I was forced to wait because a message from the future could not enter this domain. Here was pure, timeless nature—sequences as incomprehensible as pebbles—dropped like the shaped stones of the red men who had no history. The world eaters, by contrast, with their insatiable hunger for energy, quickly ran through nature; they felt it was exhaustible. They had, like all the spore-bearing organisms, an instinctive hunger for flight. They wanted more from the dark storehouse of a single planet than a panther's skin or a buffalo robe could offer. They wanted a greater novelty, only to be found far off in the orchard of the worlds.

Eventually, because the message never came, I went on. I could, I suppose, have been safe there. I could have continued to hesitate among the stones and been forgotten, or, because one came to know it was possible, I could simply have dissolved in the light that was of no season but eternity. In the end, I pursued my way downstream and out into the sagebrush of ordinary lands. Time reasserted its hold upon me but not quite in the usual way. Sometimes I could almost hear the thing for which I had waited in vain, or almost remember it. It was as though I carried the scar of some unusual psychical encounter.

A physician once described to me in detail the body's need to rectify its injuries, to restore, in so far as possible, mangled bones and tissues. A precisely arranged veil of skin is drawn over ancient wounds. Similarly the injured mind struggles, even in a delusory way, to reassemble and make sense of its shattered world. Whatever I had been exposed to among the snow crests and the autumn light still penetrated my being. Mine was the wound of a finite creature seeking to establish its own reality against eternity.

I am all that I have striven to describe of the strangest organism on the planet. I am one of the world eaters in the time when that species has despoiled the earth and is about to loose its spores into space. As an archaeologist I also know that our planet-effacing qualities extend to time itself. When the swarming phase of our existence commences, we struggle both against the remembered enchantment of childhood and the desire to extinguish it under layers of concrete and giant stones. Like some few persons in the days of the final urban concentrations, I am an anachronism, a child of the dying light. By those destined to create the future, my voice may not, perhaps, be trusted. I know only that I speak from the timeless country revisited, from the cold of vast tundras and the original dispersals, not from the indrawings of men.

II

The nineteenth-century novelist Thomas Love Peacock once remarked critically that "a poet in our times is a semi-barbarian in a civilized community. . . . The march of his intellect is like that of a crab, backward." It is my suspicion that though many moderns would applaud what Peacock probably meant only ironically, there is a certain virtue in the sidelong retreat of the crab. He never runs, he never ceases to face what menaces him, and he always keeps his pincers well to the fore. He is a creature adapted by nature for rearguard action and withdrawal, but never rout.

The true poet is just such a fortunate creation as the elusive crab. He is born wary and is frequently in retreat because he is a protector of the human spirit. In the fruition time of the world eaters he is threatened, not with obsolescence, but with being hunted to extinction. I rather fancy such creatures—poets, I mean—as lurking about the edge of all our activities, testing with a probing eye, if not claw, our thoughts as well as our machines. Blake was right about the double vision of poets. There is no substitute, in a future-oriented society, for eyes on stalks, or the ability to move suddenly at right angles from some dimly imminent catastrophe. The spore bearers, once they have reached the departure stage, are impatient of any but acceptable prophets—prophets, that is, of the swarming time. These are the men who uncritically proclaim our powers over the cosmic prison and who dangle before us ill-assorted keys to the gate.

By contrast, one of the most perceptive minds in American literature, Ralph Waldo Emerson, once maintained stubbornly: "The soul is no traveller." Emerson spoke in an era when it was a passion with American writers to go abroad, just as today many people yearn for the experience of space. He was not engaged in deriding the benefits of travel. The wary poet merely persisted in the recognition that the soul in its creative expression is genuinely *not* a traveler, that the great writer is peculiarly a product of his native environment. As an untraveled traveler, he picks up selectively from his surroundings a fiery train of dissimilar memory particles—"unlike things" which are woven at last into the likeness of truth.

Man's urge toward transcendence manifests itself even in his outward inventions. However crudely conceived, his rockets, his cyborgs, are intended to leap some void, some recently discovered chasm before him, even as long ago he cunningly devised language to reach across the light-year distances between individual minds. The spore bearers of thought have a longer flight history than today's astronauts. They found, fantastic though it now seems, the keys to what originally appeared to be the impregnable prison of selfhood.

But these ancient word-flight specialists the poets have another skill that enhances their power beyond even the contemporary ability they have always had to sway minds. They have, in addition, a preternatural sensitivity to the backward and forward reaches of time. They probe into life as far as, if not farther than, the molecular biologist does, because they touch life itself and not its particulate structure. The latter is a recent scientific disclosure, and hence we acclaim the individual discoverers. The poets, on the other hand, have been talking across the ages until we have come to take their art for granted. It is useless to characterize them as dealers in the obsolete, because this venerable, word-loving trait in man is what enables him to transmit his eternal hunger—his yearning for the country of the unchanging autumn light. Words are man's domain, from his beginning to his fall.

Many years ago I chanced to read a story by Don Stuart entitled "Twilight." It is an account of the further history of humanity many millions of years in the future. The story is told by a man a few centuries beyond our time, who in the course of an experiment had been accidentally projected forward into the evening of the race. He had then escaped through his own powers, but in doing so had overleaped his own era and reached our particular century. The time voyager sings an unbearably sad song learned in that remote future—a song that called and sought and searched in hopelessness. It was the song of man in his own twilight, a song of the final autumn when hope had gone and man's fertility with it, though he continued to linger on in the shadow of the perfect machines which he had created and which would long outlast him.

What lifts this story beyond ordinary science fiction is its compassionate insight into the basic nature of the race —the hunger that had accompanied man to his final intellectual triumph in earth's garden cities. There he had lost the will and curiosity to seek any further to transcend himself. Instead, that passion had been lavished upon his great machines. But the songs wept and searched for something that had been forgotten—something that could never be found again. The man from the open noonday of the human triumph, the scientist of the thirty-first century, before seeking his own return down the time channel, carries out one final act that is symbolic of man's yearning and sense of inadequacy before the universe, even though he had wished, like Emerson, "to climb the steps of paradise." Man had failed in the end to sanctify his own being.

The indomitable time voyager standing before the deathless machines performs the last great act of the human twilight. He programs the instruments to work toward the creation of a machine which would incorporate what man by then had lost: curiosity and hope. In dying, man had transmitted his hunger to the devices which had contributed to his death. Is this act to be labeled triumph or defeat? We do not learn; we are too far down in time's dim morning. The poet speaks with man's own Delphic ambiguity. We are left wondering whether the time voyager had produced the only possible solution to the final decay of humanity—that is, the transference of human values to the world of imperishable machines—or, on the other hand, whether less reliance upon the machine might have prevented the decay of the race. These are questions that only the long future will answer, but "Twilight" is a magnificent evocation of man's ending that only a poet of this century could have adequately foreseen—that man in the end forgets the message that started him upon his journey.

III

On a planet where snow falls, the light changes, and when the light changes all is changed, including life. I am not speaking now of daytime things but of the first snows of winter that always leave an intimation in each drifting flake of a thousand-year turn toward a world in which summer may sometime forget to come back. The world has known such episodes: it has not always been the world it is. Snow like a vast white amoeba has descended at intervals from the mountains and crept over the hills and valleys of the continents, ingesting forests and spewing forth boulders.

Something still touches me from that vanished world as remote from us in years as an earth rocket would be from

Alpha Centauri. Certainly Cocteau spoke the truth: to add to all the cosmic prisons that surround us there is the prison of the golden light that changes in the head of man —the light that cries to memory out of vanished worlds, the leaf-fall light of the earth's eternally changing theatre. And then comes the night snow that in some late hour transports us into that other, that vanished but unvanquished, world of the frost.

Near my house in the suburbs is a remaining fragment of woodland. It once formed part of a wealthy man's estate, and in one corner of the wood a huge castle created by imported workmen still looms among the trees that have long outlasted their original owner. A path runs through these woods and the people of multiplying suburbia hurry past upon it. For a long time I had feared for the trees.

One night it snowed and then a drop in temperature brought on the clear night sky. Dressed in a heavy sheepskin coat and galoshes, I had ventured out toward midnight upon the path through the wood. Out of old habit I studied the tracks upon the snow. People had crunched by on their way to the train station, but no human trace ran into the woods. Many little animals had ventured about the margin of the trees, perhaps timidly watching; none had descended to the path. On impulse, for I had never done so before in this spot, I swung aside into the world of no human tracks. At first it pleased me that the domain of the wood had remained so far untouched and undesecrated. Did man still, after all his ravages, possess some fear of the midnight forest or some unconscious reverence toward the source of his origins? It seemed hardly likely in so accessible a spot, but I trudged on, watching the pole star through the naked branches. Here, I tried to convince myself, was a fragment of the older world, something that had momently escaped the eye of the world eaters.

After a time I came to a snow-shrouded clearing, and because my blood is, after all, that of the spore bearers, I sheltered my back against an enormous oak and continued to watch for a long time the circling of remote constellations above my head. Perhaps somewhere across the void another plotting eye on a similar midnight errand might be searching this arm of the galaxy. Would our eyes meet? I smiled a little uncomfortably and let my eyes drop, still unseeing and lost in contemplation, to the snow about me. The cold continued to deepen.

We were a very young race, I meditated, and of civilizations that had yet reached the swarming stage there had been but few. They had all been lacking in some aspect of the necessary technology, and their doom had come swift upon them before they had grasped the nature of the cosmos toward which they unconsciously yearned.

Egypt, which had planted in the pyramids man's mightiest challenge to effacing time, had conceived long millennia ago the dream of a sky-traveling boat that might reach the pole star. The Maya of the New World rain forests had also watched the drift of the constellations from their temples situated above the crawling vegetational sea about them. But of what their dreamers thought, the remaining hieroglyphs tell us little. We know only that the Maya were able to grope with mathematical accuracy through unlimited millions of years of which Christian Europe had no contemporary comprehension. The lost culture had remarkably accurate eclipse tables and precise time-commemorating monuments.

Ironically the fragments of those great stelae with all

their learned calculations were, in the end, to be dragged about and worshiped upside down by a surviving peasantry who had forgotten their true significance. I, in this wintry clime under the shifting of the Bear, would no more be able to enter the mythology of that world of vertical time than to confront whatever eye might roam the dust clouds at this obscure corner of the galaxy. So it was, in turning, that I gazed in full consciousness at last upon the starlit clearing that surrounded me.

Except for the snow, I might as well have been standing upon the ruins that had thronged my mind. The clearing was artificial, a swath slashed by instruments of war through the center of the wood. Shorn trees toppled by bulldozers lay beneath the snow. Piles of rusted machinery were cast indiscriminately among the fallen trees. I came forward, groping like the last man out of a shell hole in some giant, unseen conflict. Iron, rust, timbers—the place was like the graveyard of an unseen, incessant war.

In the starlight my eye caught a last glimpse of living green. I waded toward the object but it lay upon its side. I rolled it over. It was a still-living Christmas tree hurled out with everything dispensable from an apartment house at the corner of the wood. I stroked it in wordless apology. Like others, I had taken the thin screen remaining from the original wood for reality. Only the snow, only the tiny footprints of the last surviving wood creatures, had led me to this unmasking. Behind this little stand of trees the world eaters had all the time been assiduously at work.

Well, and why not, countered my deviant slime-mold mind? The sooner men finished the planet, the sooner the spores would have to fly. I kicked vaguely at some geared piece of mechanism under its cover of snow. I thought of the last Mayan peasants worshiping the upended mathematical tablets of their forerunners. The supposition persisted in the best scientific circles that the astronomer priests had in the end proved too great a burden, they and their temples and observatories too expensive a luxury for their society to maintain — that revolt had cut them down.

But what if, a voice whispered at the back of my mind, as though the indistinct cosmic figure I had earlier conjured up had just spoken, what if during all that thousand years of computing among heavy unnatural numbers, they had found a way to clamber through some hidden galactic doorway? Would it not have been necessary to abandon these monumental cities and leave their illiterate worshipers behind?

I turned over a snow-covered cogwheel. Who, after all, among such ruins could be sure that we were the first of the planet viruses to depart? Perhaps in the numbers and the hieroglyphs of long ago there had been hidden some other formula than that based upon the mathematics of rocket travel—some key to a doorway of air, leaving behind only the empty seedpods of the fallen cities. Slowly my mind continued to circle that dead crater under the winter sky.

Suppose, my thought persisted, there is still another answer to the ruins in the rain forests of Yucatan, or to the incised brick tablets baking under the Mesopotamian sun. Suppose that greater than all these, vaster and more impressive, an invisible pyramid lies at the heart of every civilization man has created, that for every visible brick or corbeled vault or upthrust skyscraper or giant rocket we bear a burden in the mind to excess, that we have a biologi-

Man in the Autumn Light ∗ 131

cal urge to complete what is actually uncompletable.

Every civilization, born like an animal body, has just so much energy to expend. In its birth throes it chooses a path, the pathway perhaps of a great religion as in the time when Christianity arose. Or an empire of thought is built among the Greeks, or a great power extends its roads, and governs as did the Romans. Or again, its wealth is poured out upon science, and science endows the culture with great energy, so that far goals seem attainable and yet grow illusory. Space and time widen to weariness. In the midst of triumph disenchantment sets in among the young. It is as though with the growth of cities an implosion took place, a final unseen structure, a spore-bearing structure towering upward toward its final release.

Men talked much of progress and enlightenment on the path behind the thin screen of trees. I myself had walked there in the cool mornings awaiting my train to the city. All the time this concealed gash in the naked earth had been growing. I was wrong in just one thing in my estimate of civilization. I have said it is born like an animal and so, in a sense, it is. But an animal is whole. The secret tides of its body balance and sustain it until death. They draw it to its destiny. The great cultures, by contrast, have no final homeostatic feedback like that of the organism. They appear to have no destiny unless it is that of the slime mold's destiny to spore and depart. Too often they grow like a malignancy, in one direction only. The Maya had calculated the drifting eons like gods but they did not devise a single wheeled vehicle. So distinguished an authority as Eric Thompson has compared them to an overspecialized Jurassic monster.

A monster? My eyes swept slowly over the midnight clearing and its hidden refuse of fallen trunks and cogwheels. This was the pyramid that our particular culture was in the process of creating. It represented energy beyond anything the world of man had previously known. Our first spore flight had burst against the moon and reached, even now, toward Mars, but its base was a slime-mold base—the spore base of the world eaters. They fed upon the world, and the resources they consumed would never be duplicable again because their base was finite. Neither would the planet long sustain this tottering pyramid thrust upward from what had once been the soil of a consumed forest.

A rising wind began to volley snow across the clearing, burying deeper the rusted wheels and shrieking over the cast-off tree of Christmas. There was a hint in the chill air of a growing implacable winter, like that which finally descends upon an outworn planet—a planet from which life and oxygen are long since gone.

I returned to the shelter of the oak, my gaze sweeping as I did so the night sky of earth, now dark and overcast. It came to me then, in a lonely surge of feeling, that I was childless and my destiny not bound to my kind. With the tough oak at my back I remembered the feel of my father's face against my own on the night I had seen Halley's star. The comet had marked me. I was a citizen and a scientist of that nation which had first reached the moon. There in the ruined wood, remembering the shrunken seedpods of dead cities, I yearned silently toward those who would come after me if the race survived.

Four hundred years ago a young poet and potential rival

of Shakespeare had written of the knowledge-hungry
Faust of legend:

> Thou art still but Faustus
> and a man.

In that phrase Christopher Marlowe had epitomized the
human tragedy: We were world eaters and knowledge
seekers but we were also men. It was a well-nigh fatal flaw.
Whether we, like the makers of stone spearpoints in Wyoming, are a fleeting illusion of the autumn light depends
upon whether any remain to decipher Marlowe's words
one thousand years in the future.

The events of my century had placed the next millennium as far off as a star. All the elaborate mechanisms of
communication we have devised have not ennobled, nor
brought closer, individual men to men. The means exist.
It is Faustus who remains a man. Beyond this dark, I, who
was also a man, could not penetrate.

In the deepening snow I made a final obeissance to the
living world. I took the still green, everlasting tree home
to my living room for Christmas rites that had not been
properly accorded it. I suppose the act was blindly compulsive. It was the sort of thing that Peacock in his time would
have termed the barbarism of poets.

SEVEN ‡ THE LAST MAGICIAN

The human heart is local and finite, it has roots,
and if the intellect radiates from it, according to
its strength, to greater and greater distances, the
reports, if they are to be gathered up at all,
must be gathered at the center.

—GEORGE SANTAYANA

THE LAST MAGICIAN

Every man in his youth—and who is to say when youth is ended?—meets for the last time a magician, the man who made him what he is finally to be. In the mass, man now confronts a similar magician in the shape of his own collective brain, that unique and spreading force which in its manipulations will precipitate the last miracle, or, like the sorcerer's apprentice, wreak the last disaster. The possible nature of the last disaster the world of today has made all too evident: man has become a spreading blight which threatens to efface the green world that created him.

It is of the last miracle, however, that I would write. To do so I have to describe my closing encounter with the personal magician of my youth, the man who set his final seal upon my character. To tell the tale is symbolically to establish the nature of the human predicament: how nature is to be reentered; how man, the relatively unthinking and proud creator of the second world—the world of culture—may revivify and restore the first world which cherished and brought him into being.

I was fifty years old when my youth ended, and it was, of all unlikely places, within that great unwieldy structure built to last forever and then hastily to be torn down—the Pennsylvania Station in New York. I had come in through a side doorway and was slowly descending a great staircase in a slanting shaft of afternoon sunlight. Distantly I became aware of a man loitering at the bottom of the steps, as though awaiting me there. As I descended he swung about and began climbing toward me.

At the instant I saw his upturned face my feet faltered and I almost fell. I was walking to meet a man ten years dead and buried, a man who had been my teacher and confidant. He had not only spread before me as a student the wild background of the forgotten past but had brought alive for me the spruce-forest primitives of today. With him I had absorbed their superstitions, handled their sacred objects, accepted their prophetic dreams. He had been a man of unusual mental powers and formidable personality. In all my experience no dead man but he could have so wrenched time as to walk through its cleft of darkness unharmed into the light of day.

The massive brows and forehead looked up at me as if to demand an accounting of that elapsed decade during which I had held his post and discharged his duties. Unwilling step by step I descended rigidly before the baleful eyes. We met, and as my dry mouth strove to utter his name, I was aware that he was passing me as a stranger, that his gaze was directed beyond me, and that he was hastening elsewhere. The blind eye turned sidewise was not, in truth, fixed upon me; I beheld the image but not the reality of a long dead man. Phantom or genetic twin, he passed on, and the crowds of New York closed inscrutably about him.

I groped for the marble railing and braced my continued

descent. Around me travelers moved like shadows. I was a similar shadow, made so by the figure I had passed. But what was my affliction? That dead man and myself had been friends, not enemies. What terror save the terror of the living toward the dead could so powerfully have enveloped me?

On the slow train running homeward the answer came. I had been away for ten years from the forest. I had had no messages from its depths, such as that dead savant had hoarded even in his disordered office where box turtles wandered over the littered floor. I had been immersed in the postwar administrative life of a growing university. But all the time some accusing spirit, the familiar of the last wood-struck magician, had lingered in my brain. Finally exteriorized, he had stridden up the stair to confront me in the autumn light. Whether he had been imposed in some fashion upon a convenient facsimile or was a genuine illusion was of little importance compared to the message he had brought. I had starved and betrayed myself. It was this that had brought the terror. For the first time in years I left my office in midafternoon and sought the sleeping silence of a nearby cemetery. I was as pale and drained as the Indian pipe plants without chlorophyll that rise after rains on the forest floor. It was time for a change. I wrote a letter and studied time tables. I was returning to the land that bore me.

Collective man is now about to enter upon a similar though more difficult adventure. At the climactic moment of his journey into space he has met himself at the doorway of the stars. And the looming shadow before him has pointed backward into the entangled gloom of a forest from which it has been his purpose to escape. Man has crossed, in his history, two worlds. He must now enter another and forgotten one, but with the knowledge gained on the pathway to the moon. He must learn that, whatever his powers as a magician, he lies under the spell of a greater and a green enchantment which, try as he will, he can never avoid, however far he travels. The spell has been laid on him since the beginning of time—the spell of the natural world from which he sprang.

II

Long ago Plato told the story of the cave and the chained prisoners whose knowledge consisted only of what they could learn from flickering shadows on the wall before them. Then he revealed their astonishment upon being allowed to see the full source of the light. He concluded that the mind's eye may be bewildered in two ways, either from advancing suddenly into the light of higher things or descending once more from the light into the shadows. Perhaps more than Plato realized in the spinning of his myth, man has truly emerged from a cave of shadows, or from comparable leaf-shadowed dells. He has read his way into the future by firelight and by moonlight, for, in man's early history, night was the time for thinking, and for the observation of the stars. The stars traveled, men noted, and therefore they were given hunters' names. All things moved and circled. It was the way of the hunters' world and of the seasons.

In spite of much learned discourse upon the ways of our

animal kin, and of how purely instinctive cries slowly gave way to variable and muddled meanings in the head of proto-man, I like to think that the crossing into man's second realm of received wisdom was truly a magical experience.

I once journeyed for several days along a solitary stretch of coast. By the end of that time, from the oddly fractured shells on the beach, little distorted faces began to peer up at me with meaning. I had held no converse with a living thing for many hours. As a result I was beginning, in the silence, to read again, to read like an illiterate. The reading had nothing to do with sound. The faces in the cracked shells were somehow assuming a human significance.

Once again, in the night, as I traversed a vast plain on foot, the clouds that coursed above me in the moonlight began to build into archaic, voiceless pictures. That they could do so in such a manner makes me sure that the reading of such pictures has long preceded what men of today call language. The reading of so endless an alphabet of forms is already beyond the threshold of the animal; man could somehow see a face in a shell or a pointing finger in a cloud. He had both magnified and contracted his person in a way verging on the uncanny. There existed in the growing cortex of man, in its endless ramifications and prolonged growth, a place where, paradoxically, time both flowed and lingered, where mental pictures multiplied and transposed themselves. One is tempted to believe, whether or not it is literally true, that the moment of first speech arrived in a star burst like a supernova. To be sure, the necessary auditory discrimination and memory tracts were a biological preliminary, but the "invention" of language—and I put this carefully, having respect for both the biological and cultural elements involved—may have come, at the last, with rapidity.

Certainly the fossil record of man is an increasingly strange one. Millions of years were apparently spent on the African and Asiatic grasslands, with little or no increase in brain size, even though simple tools were in use. Then quite suddenly in the million years or so of Ice Age time the brain cells multiply fantastically. One prominent linguist would place the emergence of true language at no more than forty thousand years ago. I myself would accord it a much longer history, but all scholars would have to recognize biological preparation for its emergence. What the fossil record, and perhaps even the studies of living primates, will never reveal is how much can be attributed to slow incremental speech growth associated directly with the expanding brain, and how much to the final cultural innovation spreading rapidly to other biologically prepared groups.

Language, wherever it first appeared, is the cradle of the human universe, a universe displaced from the natural in the common environmental sense of the word. In this second world of culture, forms arise in the brain and can be transmitted in speech as words are found for them. Objects and men are no longer completely within the world we call natural—they are subject to the transpositions which the brain can evoke or project. The past can be remembered and caused to haunt the present. Gods may murmur in the trees, or ideas of cosmic proportions can twine a web of sustaining mathematics around the cosmos.

In the attempt to understand his universe, man has to

give away a part of himself which can never be regained —the certainty of the animal that what it senses is actually there in the shape the eye beholds. By contrast, man finds himself in Plato's cave of illusion. He has acquired an interest in the whole of the natural world at the expense of being ejected from it and returning, all too frequently, as an angry despoiler.

A distinction, however, should be made here. In his first symbol making, primitive man—and indeed even the last simple hunting cultures of today—projected a friendly image upon animals: animals talked among themselves and thought rationally like men; they had souls. Men might even have been fathered by totemic animals. Man was still existing in close interdependence with his first world, though already he had developed a philosophy, a kind of oracular "reading" of its nature. Nevertheless he was still inside that world; he had not turned it into an instrument or a mere source of materials.

Christian man in the West strove to escape this lingering illusion that the primitives had projected upon nature. Intent upon the destiny of his own soul, and increasingly urban, man drew back from too great intimacy with the natural, its fertility and its orgiastic attractions. If the new religion was to survive, Pan had to be driven from his hillside or rendered powerless by incorporating him into Christianity—to be baptized, in other words, and allowed to fade slowly from the memory of the folk. As always in such intellectual upheavals, something was gained and something lost.

What was gained intellectually was a monotheistic reign of law by a single deity so that man no longer saw distinct and powerful spirits in every tree or running brook. His animal confreres slunk like pariahs soulless from his presence. They no longer spoke, their influence upon man was broken; the way was unconsciously being prepared for the rise of modern science. That science, by reason of its detachment, would first of all view nature as might a curious stranger. Finally it would, while giving powers to man, turn upon him also the same gaze that had driven the animal forever into the forest. Man, too, would be subject to what he had evoked; he, too, in a new fashion, would be relegated soulless to the wood with all his lurking irrationalities exposed. He would know in a new and more relentless fashion his relationship to the rest of life. Yet as the growing crust of his exploitive technology thickened, the more man thought that he could withdraw from or recast nature, that by drastic retreat he could dispel his deepening sickness.

Like that of one unfortunate scientist I know—a remorseless experimenter—man's whole face had grown distorted. One eye, one bulging eye, the technological, scientific eye, was willing to count man as well as nature's creatures in terms of megadeaths. Its objectivity had become so great as to endanger its master, who was mining his own brains as ruthlessly as a seam of coal. At last Ortega y Gasset was to remark despairingly, "There is no human nature, there is only history." That history, drawn from man's own brain and subject to his power to transpose reality, now looms before us as future on all the confines of the world.

Linguists have a word for the power of language: displacement. It is the way by which man came to survive in nature. It is also the method by which he created and entered his second world, the realm that now encloses him. In addition, it is the primary instrument by which he developed the means to leave the planet earth. It is a very mysterious achievement whose source is none other than the ghostly symbols moving along the ramifying pathways of the human cortex, the gray enfolded matter of the brain. Displacement, in simple terms, is the ability to talk about what is absent, to make use of the imaginary in order to control reality. Man alone is able to manipulate time into past and future, transpose objects or abstract ideas in a similar fashion, and make a kind of reality which is not present, or which exists only as potential in the real world.

From this gift comes his social structure and traditions and even the tools with which he modifies his surroundings. They exist in the dark confines of the cranium before the instructed hand creates the reality. In addition, and as a corollary of displacement, language is characterized by the ability to receive constant increments and modifications. Words drop into or out of use, or change their meanings. The constant easy ingestion of the new, in spite of the stability of grammatical structure, is one of the prime characteristics of language. It is a structured instrument which at the same time reveals an amazing flexibility. This flexibility allows us a distant glimpse of the endlessly streaming shadows that make up the living brain.

III

There is another aspect of man's mental life which demands the utmost attention, even though it is manifest in different degrees in different times and places and among

different individuals; this is the desire for transcendence—
a peculiarly human trait. Philosophers and students of
comparative religion have sometimes remarked that we
need to seek for the origins of the human interest in the
cosmos, "a cosmic sense" unique to man. However this
sense may have evolved, it has made men of the greatest
imaginative power conscious of human inadequacy and
weakness. There may thus emerge the desire for "rebirth"
expressed in many religions. Stimulated by his own un-
completed nature, man seeks a greater role, restructured
beyond nature like so much in his aspiring mind. Thus we
find the Zen Buddhist, in the words of the scholar Suzuki,
intent upon creating "a realm of Emptiness or Void where
no conceptualism prevails" and where "rootless trees
grow." The Buddhist, in a true paradox, would empty the
mind in order that the mind may adequately receive or
experience the world. No other creature than man would
question his way of thought or feel the need of sweeping
the mind's cloudy mirror in order to unveil its insight.

Man's life, in other words, is felt to be unreal and sterile.
Perhaps a creature of so much ingenuity and deep memory
is almost bound to grow alienated from his world, his
fellows, and the objects around him. He suffers from a
nostalgia for which there is no remedy upon earth except
as it is to be found in the enlightenment of the spirit—some
ability to have a perceptive rather than an exploitive relationship with his fellow creatures.

After man had exercised his talents in the building of the
first neolithic cities and empires, a period mostly marked
by architectural and military triumphs, an intellectual
transformation descended upon the known world, a time
of questioning. This era is fundamental to an understand-

ing of man, and has engaged the attention of such modern scholars as Karl Jaspers and Lewis Mumford. The period culminates in the first millennium before Christ. Here in the great centers of civilization, whether Chinese, Indian, Judaic, or Greek, man had begun to abandon inherited gods and purely tribal loyalties in favor of an inner world in which the pursuit of earthly power was ignored. The destiny of the human soul became of more significance than the looting of a province. Though these dreams are expressed in different ways by such divergent men as Christ, Buddha, Lao-tse, and Confucius, they share many things in common, not the least of which is respect for the dignity of the common man.

The period of the creators of transcendent values—the axial thinkers, as they are called—created the world of universal thought that is our most precious human heritage. One can see it emerging in the mind of Christ as chronicled by Saint John. Here the personalized tribal deity of earlier Judaic thought becomes transformed into a world deity. Christ, the Good Shepherd, says: "Other sheep I have, which are not of this fold: them also I must bring, and they shall hear my voice; and there shall be one fold and one shepherd. . . . My sheep hear my voice . . . and they follow me."

These words spoken by the carpenter from Nazareth are those of a world changer. They passed boundaries, whispered in the ears of galley slaves: "One fold, one shepherd. Follow me." These are no longer the wrathful words of a jealous city ravager, a local potentate god. They mark instead, in the high cultures, the rise of a new human image, a rejection of purely material goals, a turning toward some inner light. As these ideas diffused, they were, of course, subject to the wear of time and superstition, but the human ethic of the individual prophets and thinkers has outlasted empires.

Such men speak to us across the ages. In their various approaches to life they encouraged the common man toward charity and humility. They did not come with weapons; instead they bespoke man's purpose to subdue his animal nature and in so doing to create a radiantly new and noble being. These were the dreams of the first millennium B.C. Tormented man, arising, falling, still pursues those dreams today.

Earlier I mentioned Plato's path into the light that blinds the man who has lived in darkness. Out of just such darkness arose the first humanizing influence. It was genuinely the time of the good shepherds. No one can clearly determine why these prophets had such profound effects within the time at their disposal. Nor can we solve the mystery of how they came into existence across the Euro-Asiatic land mass in diverse cultures at roughly the same time. As Jaspers observes, he who can solve this mystery will know something common to all mankind.

In this difficult era we are still living in the inspirational light of a tremendous historical event, one that opened up the human soul. But if the neophytes were blinded by the light, so, perhaps, the prophets were in turn confused by the human darkness they encountered. The scientific age replaced them. The common man, after brief days of enlightenment, turned once again to escape, propelled outward first by the world voyagers, and then by the atom breakers. We have called up vast powers which loom menacingly over us. They await our bidding, and we turn to outer space as though the solitary answer to the unspoken query must be flight, such flight as ancient man engaged in across ice ages and vanished game trails—the flight from nowhere.

The good shepherds meantime have all faded into the darkness of history. One of them, however, left a cryptic message: "My doctrine is not mine but his that sent me." Even in the time of unbelieving this carries a warning. For He that sent may still be couched in the body of man awaiting the end of the story.

IV

When I was a small boy I once lived near a brackish stream that wandered over the interminable salt flats south of our town. Between occasional floods the area became a giant sunflower forest, taller than the head of a man. Child gangs roved this wilderness, and guerrilla combats with sunflower spears sometimes took place when boys from the other side of the marsh ambushed the hidden trails. Now and then, when a raiding party sought a new path, one could see from high ground the sunflower heads shaking and closing over the passage of the life below. In some such manner nature's green barriers must have trembled and subsided in silence behind the footsteps of the first man-apes who stumbled out of the vine-strewn morass of centuries into the full sunlight of human consciousness.

The sunflower forest of personal and racial childhood is relived in every human generation. One reaches the high ground, and all is quiet in the shaken reeds. The nodding golden flowers spring up indifferently behind us, and the

The Last Magician ✴ 149

way backward is lost when finally we turn to look. There is something unutterably secretive involved in man's intrusion into his second world, into the mutable domain of thought. Perhaps he questions still his right to be there.

Some act unknown, some propitiation of unseen forces, is demanded of him. For this purpose he has raised pyramids and temples, but all in vain. A greater sacrifice is demanded, the act of a truly great magician, the man capable of transforming himself. For what, increasingly, is required of man is that he pursue the paradox of return. So desperate has been the human emergence from fen and thicket, so great has seemed the virtue of a single magical act carried beyond nature, that man hesitates, as long ago I had similarly shuddered to confront a phantom on a stair.

Written deep in the human subconscious is a simple terror of what has come with us from the forest and sometimes haunts our dreams. Man does not wish to retrace his steps down to the margin of the reeds and peer within, lest by some magic he be permanently recaptured. Instead, men prefer to hide in cities of their own devising. I know a New Yorker who, when she visits the country, complains that the crickets keep her awake. I knew another who had to be awakened screaming from a nightmare of whose nature he would never speak. As for me, a long-time student of the past, I, too, have had my visitants.

The dreams are true. By no slight effort have we made our way through the marshes. Something unseen has come along with each of us. The reeds sway shut, but not as definitively as we would wish. It is the price one pays for bringing almost the same body through two worlds. The animal's needs are very old; it must sometimes be coaxed into staying in its new discordant realm. As a consequence all religions have realized that the soul must not be allowed to linger yearning at the edge of the sunflower forest.

The curious sorcery of sound symbols and written hieroglyphs in man's new brain had to be made to lure him farther and farther from the swaying reeds. Temples would better contain his thought and fix his dreams upon the stars in the night sky. A creature who has once passed from visible nature into the ghostly insubstantial world evolved and projected from his own mind will never cease to pursue thereafter the worlds beyond this world. Nevertheless the paradox remains: man's crossing into the realm of space has forced him equally to turn and contemplate with renewed intensity the world of the sunflower forest —the ancient world of the body that he is doomed to inhabit, the body that completes his cosmic prison.

Not long ago I chanced to fly over a forested section of country which, in my youth, was still an unfrequented wilderness. Across it now suburbia was spreading. Below, like the fungus upon a fruit, I could see the radiating lines of transport gouged through the naked earth. From far up in the wandering air one could see the lines stretching over the horizon. They led to cities clothed in an unmoving haze of smog. From my remote, abstract position in the clouds I could gaze upon all below and watch the incipient illness as it spread with all its slimy tendrils through the watershed.

Farther out, I knew, on the astronauts' track, the earth would hang in silver light and the seas hold their ancient blue. Man would be invisible; the creeping white rootlets of his urban growth would be equally unseen. The blue, cloud-covered planet would appear still as when the first men stole warily along a trail in the forest. Upon one thing, however, the scientists of the space age have informed us. Earth is an inexpressibly unique possession. In the entire solar system it alone possesses water and oxygen sufficient to nourish higher life. It alone contains the seeds of mind. Mercury bakes in an inferno of heat beside the sun; something strange has twisted the destiny of Venus; Mars is a chill desert; Pluto is a cold wisp of reflected light over three billion miles away on the edge of the black void. Only on earth does life's green engine fuel the oxygen-devouring brain.

For centuries we have dreamed of intelligent beings throughout this solar system. We have been wrong; the earth we have taken for granted and treated so casually—the sunflower-shaded forest of man's infancy—is an incredibly precious planetary jewel. We are all of us—man, beast, and growing plant—aboard a space ship of limited dimensions whose journey began so long ago that we have abandoned one set of gods and are now in the process of substituting another in the shape of science.

The axial religions had sought to persuade man to transcend his own nature; they had pictured to him limitless perspectives of self-mastery. By contrast, science in our time has opened to man the prospect of limitless power over exterior nature. Its technicians sometimes seem, in fact, to have proffered us the power of the void as though flight were the most important value on earth.

"We have got to spend everything we have, if necessary, to get off this planet," one such representative of the aerospace industry remarked to me recently.

"Why?" I asked, not averse to flight, but a little bewildered by his seeming desperation.

"Because," he insisted, his face turning red as though

from some deep inner personal struggle, "because"—then he flung at me what I suspect he thought my kind of science would take seriously—"because of the ice—the ice is coming back, that's why."

Finally, as though to make everything official, one of the space agency administrators was quoted in *Newsweek* shortly after the astronauts had returned from the moon: "Should man," this official said, "fall back from his destiny . . . the confines of this planet will destroy him."

It was a strange way to consider our planet, I thought, closing the magazine and brooding over this sudden distaste for life at home. Why was there this hidden anger, this inner flight syndrome, these threats for those who remained on earth? Some powerful, not totally scientific impulse seemed tugging at the heart of man. Was it fear of his own mounting numbers, the creeping of the fungus threads? But where, then, did these men intend to flee? The solar system stretched bleak and cold and crater-strewn before my mind. The nearest, probably planetless star was four light-years and many human generations away. I held up the magazine once more. Here and here alone, photographed so beautifully from space, was the blue jewel compounded of water and of living green. Yet upon the page the words repeated themselves: "This planet will destroy him."

No, I thought, this planet nourished man. It took four million years to find our way through the sunflower forest, and after that only a few millennia to reach the moon. It is not fair to say this planet will destroy us. Space flight is a brave venture, but upon the soaring rockets are projected all the fears and evasions of man. He had fled across two worlds, from the windy corridors of wild savannahs to the sunlit world of the mind, and still he flees. Earth will not destroy him. It is he who threatens to destroy the earth. In sober terms we are forced to reflect that by enormous expenditure and effort we have ventured a small way out into the planetary system of a minor star, but an even smaller way into the distances, no less real, that separate man from man.

Creatures who evolve as man has done sometimes bear the scar tissue of their evolutionary travels in their bodies. The human cortex, the center of high thought, has come to dominate, but not completely to suppress, the more ancient portions of the animal brain. Perhaps it was from this last wound that my engineer friend was unconsciously fleeing. We know that within our heads there still exists an irrational restive ghost that can whisper disastrous messages into the ear of reason.

During the axial period, as we have noted, several great religions arose in Asia. For the first time in human history man's philosophical thinking seems to have concerned itself with universal values, with man's relation to man across the barriers of empire or tribal society. A new ethic, not even now perfected, struggled to emerge from the human mind. To these religions of self-sacrifice and disdain of worldly power men were drawn in enormous numbers. Though undergoing confused erosion in our time, they still constitute the primary allegiance of many millions of the world's population.

Today man's mounting numbers and his technological power to pollute his environment reveal a single demanding necessity: the necessity for him consciously to reenter and preserve, for his own safety, the old first world from which he originally emerged. His second world, drawn from his own brain, has brought him far, but it cannot take him out of nature, nor can he live by escaping into his second world alone. He must now incorporate from the wisdom of the axial thinkers an ethic not alone directed toward his fellows, but extended to the living world around him. He must make, by way of his cultural world, an actual conscious reentry into the sunflower forest he had thought merely to exploit or abandon. He must do this in order to survive. If he succeeds he will, perhaps, have created a third world which combines elements of the original two and which should bring closer the responsibilities and nobleness of character envisioned by the axial thinkers who may be acclaimed as the creators, if not of man, then of his soul. They expressed, in a prescientific era, man's hunger to transcend his own image, a hunger not entirely submerged even beneath the formidable weaponry and technological triumphs of the present.

The story of the great saviors, whether Chinese, Indian, Greek, or Judaic, is the story of man in the process of enlightening himself, not simply by tools, but through the slow inward growth of the mind that made and may yet master them through knowledge of itself. "The poet, like the lightning rod," Emerson once stated, "must reach from a point nearer the sky than all surrounding objects down to the earth, and into the dark wet soil, or neither is of use." Today that effort is demanded not only of the poet. In the age of space it is demanded of all of us. Without it there can be no survival of mankind, for man himself must be his last magician. He must seek his own way home.

The task is admittedly gigantic, but even Halley's flaming star has rounded on its track, a pinpoint of light in the uttermost void. Man, like the comet, is both bound and free. Throughout the human generations the star has always turned homeward. Nor do man's inner journeys differ from those of that far-flung elliptic. Now, as in earlier necromantic centuries, the meteors that afflicted ignorant travelers rush overhead. In the ancient years, when humankind wandered through briars and along windy precipices, it was thought well, when encountering comets or firedrakes, "to pronounce the name of God with a clear voice."

This act was performed once more by many millions when the wounded Apollo 13 swerved homeward, her desperate crew intent, if nothing else availed, upon leaving their ashes on the winds of earth. A love for earth, almost forgotten in man's roving mind, had momentarily reasserted its mastery, a love for the green meadows we have so long taken for granted and desecrated to our cost. Man was born and took shape among earth's leafy shadows. The most poignant thing the astronauts had revealed in their extremity was the nostalgic call still faintly ringing on the winds from the sunflower forest.

BIBLIOGRAPHY

BIBLIOGRAPHY

Alfvén, Hannes. *Atom, Man and the Universe: The Long Chain of Complications*. San Francisco: W.H. Freeman, 1969.
———. *Worlds—Antiworlds: Antimatter in Cosmology*. San Francisco: W.H. Freeman, 1966.

Auden, W.H. *The Dyer's Hand, and Other Essays*. New York: Random House, 1962.

Bates, Marston. *The Jungle in the House*. New York: Walker, 1970.

Benedict, Ruth, *Patterns of Culture*. Boston: Houghton Mifflin, 1934.

Bengelsdorf, Irving S. *Spaceship Earth: People and Pollution*. Los Angeles: Fox-Mathis Publications, 1969.

Berndt, R.M. and C.H. *The World of the First Australians*. Chicago: University of Chicago Press, 1964.

Bilanink, O., and Sudarshan, E.C.G. "Beyond the Light Barrier," *Physics Today*, 22 (1969), 43-51.

Bird, David, "Pollution Fight Gains in Colleges Here," *The New York Times*, February 23, 1970.

Bonner, John Tyler. *The Cellular Slime Mold*. 2nd rev. ed. Princeton: Princeton University Press, 1967.
———. "How Slime Molds Communicate," *Scientific American*, 209 (1963), 84-93.

Bridgman, P.W. "On the Nature and the Limitations of Cosmical Inquiries," *Scientific Monthly*, 37 (November 1933), 385-397.

Burton, Richard. *The Anatomy of Melancholy* [1612]. New York: Tudor, 1951.

Campbell, Joseph. *The Masks of God: I. Primitive Mythology.* New York: Viking Press, 1959.

Chamberlain, George F. *The Story of the Comets.* London: Oxford University Press, 1909.

Childe, V. Gordon. *Man Makes Himself.* New York: New American Library, 1952.

Christensen, Clyde M. *The Molds and Man: An Introduction to the Fungi.* Minneapolis: University of Minnesota Press, 1951.

Conklin, H.C. "The Relation of Hanunóo Culture to the Plant World." Doctoral dissertation. Yale University, 1954.

Cottrell, Fred. *Energy and Society.* New York: McGraw-Hill, 1955.

Cousins, Norman. "Needed: A New Dream," *Saturday Review,* June 20, 1970.

Crowther, J.G. *Francis Bacon, the First Statesman of Science.* Chester, Pa.: Dufour Editions, 1960.

Eiseley, Loren. "Francis Bacon," *Horizon,* 6 (Winter 1964), 33-47.

———. "The Paleo Indians: Their Survival and Diffusion," *New Interpretations of Aboriginal American Culture History.* Washington, D.C.: Anthropological Society of Washington, 1955.

Elder, Frederick. *Crisis in Eden: A Religious Study of Man and Environment,* New York: Abingdon Press, 1970.

Eliade, Mircea. *Patterns in Comparative Religion.* New York: Sheed and Ward, 1958.

Forbes, R.J. *The Conquest of Nature: Technology and Its Consequences.* New York: Frederick A. Praeger, 1968.

Garrett, Garet. *Ouroboros or the Mechanical Extension of Mankind.* New York: E.P. Dutton, 1925.

Gartmann, Heinz. *Science as History.* London: Hodder and Stoughton, 1961.

Glanvill, Joseph. *Scepsis Scientifica* [1665]. London: Kegan Paul, Trench, 1885.

Gold, Thomas. "Observations of a Remarkable Glazing Phenomenon on the Lunar Surface," *Science*, 165 (1969), 1345-1349.

Gooddy, William. "Outside Time and Inside Time," *Perspectives in Biology and Medicine*, 12 (1969), 239-253.

Gregory, William K. *Evolution Emerging. A Survey of Changing Patterns from Primeval Life to Man*. 2 vols. New York: Macmillan, 1951.

Grobstein, Clifford. *The Strategy of Life*. San Francisco: W.H. Freeman, 1964.

Halacy, D.S. *Cyborg: Evolution of the Superman*. New York: Harper and Row, 1965.

Hartland, E.S. *The Science of Fairy Tales: An Inquiry into Fairy Mythology* [1891]. Detroit: Singing Tree Press, 1968.

Hassan, Selim. "The Solar Boats of Khafra: Their Origin and Development Together with the Mythology of the Universe Which They are Supposed to Traverse," *Excavations at Giza*, vol. 6, part I. Cairo, Egypt: Government Press, 1960.

Herschel, Sir John. *A Preliminary Discourse on the Study of Natural Philosophy* [1830]. New York: Johnson Reprints, 1967.

Humphreys, Christmas. *Buddhism*. New York: Penguin Books, 1951.

Jaspers, Karl. *The Origin and Goal of History*. New Haven: Yale University Press, 1953.

Jepsen, Glenn L. "Time, Strata, and Fossils: Comments and Recommendations," in *Time and Stratigraphy in the Evolution of Man*. Washington, D.C.: National Academy of Sciences, National Research Council, 1967, 88-97.

Juenger, Friedrich George. *The Failure of Technology*. Chicago: Henry Regnery, 1949.

Kazantzakis, Nikos. *Report to Greco*. Translated by P.O. Bien. New York: Simon and Schuster, 1965.

Kroeber, Alfred. *Anthropology*. 2nd rev. ed. New York: Harcourt, Brace, 1948.

Lethaby, W.R. *Architecture: An Introduction.* New York: Oxford University Press, 1955.

Lévi-Strauss, Claude. *The Savage Mind.* Chicago: University of Chicago Press, 1966.

Lovell, A.C.B. *The Individual and the Universe.* New York: New American Library, 1959.

Maritain, Jacques. *Existence and the Existent.* New York: Pantheon Books, 1948.

Martz, Louis L. *The Paradise Within: Studies in Vaughn, Traherne, and Milton.* New Haven: Yale University Press, 1964.

Melville, Herman. *Moby Dick* [1851]. New York: Oxford University Press, 1947.

Mumford, Lewis. *The City in History.* New York: Harcourt, Brace & World, 1961.

————. *The Myth of the Machine.* New York: Harcourt, Brace & World, 1966.

————.*The Transformations of Man.* New York: Harcourt, Brace, 1956.

National Research Council, Committee on Resources, National Academy of Sciences. *Resources and Man: A Study and Recommendations.* San Francisco: W.H. Freeman, 1969.

Neihardt, John G. *The Stranger at the Gate.* New York: Mitchell Kennerley, 1912.

Ortega y Gasset, José. *Concord and Liberty.* New York: W.W. Norton, 1946.

Osgood, Ernest Staples (ed.). *The Field Notes of Captain William Clark 1803-1805.* New Haven: Yale University Press, 1964.

Pallatino, Massimo. *The Meaning of Archaeology.* New York: Harry N. Abrams, 1968.

Peacock, Thomas Love. "The Four Ages of Poetry," in *The Works of Thomas Love Peacock*, H. Brett-Smith and C. E. Jones (eds.), vol. 8. London: Constable, 1934.

Phillips, Henry. "On the Nature of Progress," *American Scientist,* 33 (October 1945), 253-259.

Plato. *Republic*. In *Five Great Dialogues*. Classics Club ed. Translated by Benjamin Jowett. New York: Walter J. Black, 1942.

Portman, Adolf. *New Paths in Biology*. New York: Harper and Row, 1964.

Pucetti, Roland. *Persons: A Study of the Possible Moral Agents in the Universe*. New York: Herder and Herder, 1969.

Radin, Paul, *The World of Primitive Man*. New York: Abelard Schuman, 1953.

Ritner, Peter. *The Society of Space*. New York: Macmillan, 1961.

Robertson, John M. (ed.). *The Philosophical Works of Francis Bacon*. New York: E.P. Dutton, 1905.

Ronan, Colin A. *Edmond Halley: Genius in Eclipse*. Garden City, N.Y.: Doubleday, 1969.

Santayana, George. *The Birth of Reason and Other Essays*. Daniel Cory (ed.). New York: Columbia University Press, 1968.

————. *Realms of Being*. 1 vol. ed. New York: Charles Scribner's Sons, 1942.

Shapley, Harlow. *Of Stars and Men*. Boston: Beacon Press, 1958.

Shepard, Odell. *Heart of Thoreau's Journals*. Boston: Houghton Mifflin, 1927.

Shepard, Paul, and McKinley, David (eds.). *The Subversive Science: Essays Toward an Ecology of Man*. Boston: Houghton Mifflin, 1969.

Speck, Frank G. *Naskapi*. Norman: University of Oklahoma Press, 1935.

Spengler, Oswald. *The Decline of the West*. 1 vol. ed. New York: Alfred A. Knopf, 1932.

Spiller, Robert E. *The Cycle of American Literature: An Essay in Historical Criticism*. New York: New American Library, 1957.

Still, Henry. *The Dirty Animal*. New York: Hawthorn Books, 1967.

Strehlow, T.G.H. *Aranda Traditions*. Landmarks in Anthropology Series. New York: Johnson Reprints, 1968.

Stuart, Don. "Twilight," in *The Pocket Book of Science Fiction*. Donald Wollheim (ed.). New York: Pocket Books, 1943.

Sullivan, Walter. "Moon Deposits Linked to Solar Flare," *The New York Times, September 26*, 1969.

Suzuki, Daisetz T. *The Essentials of Zen Buddhism: An Autobiography of the Writings of D.T. Suzuki*. Bernard Phillips (ed.). New York: E.P. Dutton, 1961.

Swinburne, Richard. *Space and Time*. New York: St. Martin's Press, 1968.

Thomas, Elizabeth Marshall. *The Harmless People*. New York: Random House, 1958.

Tocqueville, Alexis de. *Journey to America*. J.P. Mayer (ed.). London: Faber, 1959.

Walsh, William. *Coleridge: The Work and the Relevance*. New York: Barnes and Noble, 1967.

Whewell, William. *On the Philosophy of Discovery*. London: John W. Parker and Son, 1860.

Wilson, John A. *The Burden of Egypt*. Chicago: University of of Chicago Press, 1951.

INDEX

INDEX

Blake, William, 119, 120, 124
brain:
    evades specialization, 19-21
    increase in size during Ice
        Age time, 142
    role of in generating
        improbabilities, 20
Bruno, Giordano, 86
Buddha, saying of, 81
Buddhism, 77

C

Campbell, Joseph, 110
Carthage, 100, 101
causality, 107
Christ, Jesus, 147
Christian calendar, attempt to
    eliminate, 101
Christianity, 132
civilization, energy in, 132
civilizations:
    possibility of others in the
        cosmos, 78, 79
    resemblance to human
        personality, 103, 104
Clark, Captain William, 12
Clarke, Arthur, 55
Cocteau, Jean, 119, 128
Coleridge, Samuel Taylor,
    61, 62
collective man, encounters
    himself, 139, 140
Confucius, 147
Conklin, H. C., 58
continental divide, 13

contingency, multiplication
    of, 106
Copernicus, Nicolaus, 40
cortex, human, 141, 145, 154
cosmos, extent of, 32-38
Cree Indians, 57
cultural acceleration, 22
culture, a second world
    projected in the human
    mind, 142, 144, 145, 150,
    151, 154, 155
cyborgs, 79-82, 125
cyprinodont fish, 119, 120

D

damnatio memoriae, 100-101,
    109, 111
Darwin, Charles, 14, 18, 23, 78
Decline of the West, The, 84
dispersion, value of, 81
displacement, linguistic, 144
Donne, John, 48, 49

E

earth, as unique in solar
    system, 152
eclipse, solar, of 1970, 69
electron microscope, 88
Emerson, Ralph Waldo, 124,
    126, 155
energy, modern man's
    consumption of, 63, 64
erosion, geological, 13

ethics, extended to the world of nature, 155
evolution:
exosomatic, 80, 82
in South America and in Australia, 42-44
irreversibility of, 44
wounds of, 154
extinction, human, 79
eye, bifocal adjustment of, 119, 120

F

Faust, 85, 134
Faustian culture, Spenglerian conception of, 84, 85
Forbes, R. J., 56, 58
Frémont, John Charles, 13
Freud, Sigmund, 97

G

Galaxies, outer, 35
Galilei, Galileo, 40
Garrett, Garet, 76
geological time, perception of, 13, 14
Glanvill, Joseph, 61-63, 68
Gold, Thomas, theory of, 26, 27
Good Shepherds, time of the, 148–149
Gothic cathedrals, 84, 85
Greeks, 132

green revolution, 106
Gregory, William King, 42

H

Halley's comet, 7, 27, 32, 33, 66, 71, 133, 155-156
orbit of, 8
Hanunóo (Philippine tribe), 58, 59
history, erasure of, 100, 101; *see also damnatio memoriae*
Homo faber, 56
Homo sapiens, 64
as parasite, 54, 55, 62
Hutton, James, 13, 14

I

Ice Age, terminal fauna of, 66
invention, meaning of, 86
inventions, of power and of understanding, 86-88, 91, 92

J

Jackson, Hughlings, 20
Jaspers, Karl, 147, 148
Jepsen, Glenn, 22
John, Saint, 147
Jupiter, 70

K

Kalahari Bushmen, 70, 71
Kazantzakis, Nikos, 31
Kroeber, A. L., 20

L

language:
  development of, 142
  limitations of, 31, 32
  nature of, 20
  speculation on emergence
    of, 142
Lao-tse, 147
Lascaux, cave art of, 102
Lévi-Strauss, Claude, 59
Lewis, Meriwether, 12
linguistic displacement, 144,
  145
Lovell, Sir Bernard, 35
Lovering, Thomas, 64
Lucretius, 33, 34
Lyell, Sir Charles, 14

M

magnetic needle, 86
mammoth, belief in survival
  of, 12
man:
  alienation from nature,
    82-84
  as a bridge, 10, 11
  destiny of, 94

disrespect for nature, 70
forerunners of, 81
fossil record of, 142
as interplanetary spore
  bearer, 54
as planetary virus, 61, 64
possibility of dispersal
  through galaxies, 78, 80,
  81
retreat from nature, 144
world eater, 53-55
Maritain, Jacques, 121
Marlowe, Christopher, 133,
  134
Mars, 79, 133
Maya Indians, mathematical
  achievements of, 129, 131,
  132
Mead, Margaret, 133
Melville, Herman, 54
Mercury, 152
Mesozoic era, 42
Milky Way, galaxy of the, 35
monotheism, 143
Montagnais-Naskapi Indians,
  58
moon landings, 90, 132
mucoroides, 54
Mumford, Lewis, 63, 70, 147

N

nature:
  extravagance of, 81
  hold on man, 139, 140, 156
  primitive man's view of, 143

nature, *continued:*
   primitive and modern views
     of, 59-61
Nazareth, 147
Nixon, President Richard M.,
   77
Norman invasion, 7
North America, migration
   from, 43
North Star, 86

O

Olmec civilization, 91, 93
Origin of Species, On the, 16
Ortega y Gasset, José, 106,
   144

P

Palomar Mountain
   Observatory, 88
Pan, 143
Peacock, Thomas Love, 123,
   134
Phillips, Henry, on attempts
   to foretell the future, 108
Pilobolus, 75-77, 80
Pindar, 11
Piranesi, Giambattista, 107
Placentalia, 42
planetary impoverishment,
   danger of, 64-65
Plato, 55, 140, 143, 148
Platte river, 13

Pleistocene:
   extinction in, 24, 25
   fauna, mystery of its
     disappearance, 25-27
Pluto, 62, 152
poets, double vision of, 124
pollution, of the human
   environment, 69
Primates, of New World
   contrasted with Old, 43
primitive man:
   attitude toward nature, 143
   limitations, 58, 62, 63
prison, cosmic, nature of,
   38-45
progress, misconception of,
   104-106
proto-man:
   on African and Asiatic
     grasslands, 142
   relative antiquity of in
     comparison with *Homo
     sapiens,* 23
pyramid, invisible, 87, 93,
   131-132
pyramids, Egyptian, 87, 129

R

Radin, Paul, 114, 115
relativity theory, in relation
   to space travel, 78
rocket ship, 78
Roman empire, 77, 132
Rutherford, Sir Ernest, 78

vertebrates, 44
vestigial organs, 18

W

war, nature of modern, 68, 69
Whewell, William, 67
writing, significance of, 63,
    67
Wyoming, 120

Y

youth revolt, current, 101
Yucatan, 131

Z

Zen Buddhism, 146
zero, independent invention of
    by Maya, 86

ABOUT THE AUTHOR

Loren Eiseley, Benjamin Franklin Professor of Anthropology and the History of Science at the University of Pennsylvania in Philadelphia, spent his boyhood among the salt flats and sunflower forests of eastern Nebraska and the High Plains beyond the 99th meridian. Author of several award-winning books, Dr. Eiseley is widely known both as a naturalist and as a humanist. His work is represented in many anthologies of English prose. Dr. Eiseley has lectured at leading institutions of learning throughout the United States and has been the recipient of many honorary degrees. He serves on the Advisory Board to the National Parks system and is a past Provost of the University of Pennsylvania, as well as being Curator of Early Man in the University Museum.